D1645256

Home Guard Goings-On

Home Guard Goings-On

from

PUNCH

or the London Charivari

1940–41

by

BASIL BOOTHROYD

"Who went there?"

illustrated by

MAURICE McLOUGHLIN

LONDON

George Allen & Unwin Ltd

FIRST PUBLISHED IN 1941

Title page illustration reproduced by permission of the proprietors of PUNCH

PRINTED IN GREAT BRITAIN
in 13-Point Perpetua Type
BY UNWIN BROTHERS LIMITED
WOKING

TO MY WIFE,

WHOSE LAUGHTER IS ALWAYS IN TUNE

Acknowledgment

The author's thanks are due to the Proprietors of *Punch* for their kindness in allowing him to reproduce these articles.

Preface

The serious-minded may shake their heads over these pages. "Well," they will say—"if *that's* how they go on . . ."

Let them take heart. What they are reading, though not wholly fiction, is not the whole truth either. If the note is gay rather than grim it is only because the author has preferred the chaff to the wheat, not because the Most Amazing Army in the World lacks any part of the Churchill spirit. If it did, it would have given its fortnight's notice some time last winter, and splashed home savagely through the snow.

B. B.

Ferndown
Dorset
August 1941

Contents

I

A Little Drill

"Squa-a-a-d!" cries the colonel reedily, and we wait in amiable anticipation, all nine of us. We are the rabbits; those of our Company who went through all this twenty-five years ago are putting their rifles to more spectacular purpose elsewhere. They will come back talking earnestly of "bulls," "magpies," and other mysteries as yet hidden from us.

Presently it dawns on us that the colonel is also waiting, though less amiably. We begin to suspect that we have left undone something that we ought to have done and, wondering what this can be, we begin to squint down at our feet and rifles, and at as many other feet and rifles in the vicinity as can be not too obviously studied. One or two of us throw pride to the winds and glance frankly over our shoulders, seeking a clue in the behaviour of the rear rank.

"Azuere!" bleats the colonel unnecessarily, his patience exhausted, and he blows out his cheeks and fans himself with his green hat.

"Now, just think," he says, abandoning his parade-ground voice for one of honeyed persuasion —"you're easy now, aren't you?"

We are not easy; we are uncomfortable to a man. The evening sun is still powerful; I regret my woollen underwear and flannel shirt designed to resist the cold of the night-watch ahead of me. And there are flies.

Another source of general embarrassment is our exposed position in the main street. Our two uneven ranks are drawn up on the grass verge in full view of passers-by, and at any moment our friends, our wives, our sweethearts may cycle past and witness the exhibition that is being made of us.

We are also facing Harry Bull's boot-repairing shop, and he is regarding us with undisguised delight from his window. Harry Bull is getting a bit of his own back, for most of us have from time to time in the idle days of peace stared at him pityingly as he hammered away with his mouth full of nails.

However, we are soldiers enough to know what the colonel means, and we nod and murmur affirmatively.

"Then didn't I tell you," he says, wiping his brow on a huge yellow handkerchief, "on the word

'Squad!' to drop the right hand to the second band on your rifle? Remember?"

Of course he did! We break into relieved smiles, and nine right hands fumble quickly downwards, only to dart nervously back again at the reminder that no order has yet been given.

"Now then!" he barks suddenly, and a small eager man on the extreme left mistakes this remark for the word of command, acts upon it smartly, realizes he is alone in doing so, changes his mind, panics and drops his rifle with a clatter on the pavement in front of him. Nobody has the heart to say anything; all but the colonel are only too sensible of their own fallibility, and no doubt the colonel suppresses any spontaneous comment with the reflection that he is, after all, only the delinquent's equal in rank. Harry Bull's muffled laughter, however, comes out to us on the still evening air.

"Squa-a-a-d!"—a fluttering of hands—"*Shun!*"

The synchronization of clicking heels is not quite perfect; there is a raggedness about it, as of dying applause—but it might be worse, the colonel says. And after we have done it half a dozen times, with intermittent slopings of arms by way of variety, we all feel that it might be much worse.

The order "Right turn!" is obeyed with something approaching unanimity, and those who have misconstrued it are quick to take a hint from the rest of us; then, with a "Quick march!" and a "Left wheel!" we are sent tramping off round the corner into the comparative privacy of Pepper's Lane. We are pursued, however, by the flies, by derisive injunctions to "pick 'em up" from a few of the young villagers for whom we are planning to make democracy safe, and by the tin-trumpet barks of two odd-looking dogs who appear to have been hastily knitted in dirty white wool.

I am reprimanded en route for aiming a blow at a particularly inquisitive fly ("Don't finger your face when marching at attention!"), and the man in front of me, who has a very red neck in spite of his wearing his check cap back to front, makes the mistake of saying "What about them taters, Arthur?" to a passing cyclist. Both of us are feeling very small when finally brought to an indecisive standstill a hundred yards farther on, and no sooner have we left-turned than we get into fresh trouble for exchanging muttered words of sympathy. This, we feel, is going to take some getting used to.

When we are standing easy again, regaining our

breath (for the quick march has been rather too quick for comfort, the pace having been set by two short men manœuvred into a purely fortuitous leadership), the colonel reminds us that when standing easy we can move about as we like—except for our feet. He repeats this qualification with renewed emphasis, and I therefore stop scratching my left calf with my right shoe and further disgrace myself by springing to unbidden attention under the colonel's reproving eye. I relax, blushing, and begin to contemplate a transfer to the Auxiliary Fire Service.

Pepper's Lane is long, narrow and dusty, admirably suited, the colonel appears to think, to the perfecting of our Right-about Turn. So we do this many times, with little noticeable improvement. We are marched briskly along until everybody is in step and then turned round with four heavy stamps and marched back again. There is variety of outlook in this, if nothing else, and from time to time the check cap and red neck in front of me are replaced by the prominent shoulder-blades of the very tall man in shiny blue serge behind me. I have been wondering who it was who trod on the heels of my shoes, and now that I see the length of his legs I understand and forgive.

By now the two knitted dogs have tracked us down and are complicating matters by threading their way amongst our marching feet. They pay less attention to the colonel's words of dismissal than to our own less abstract suggestions that they

"*. . . the two knitted dogs have tracked us down . . .*"

might do better elsewhere. We are rid of them at last, though our repeated kicks at their woollen ribs have played havoc with our spacing and alignment. In a merciful spell of rest, during which we flail at the flies like two rows of miniature windmills, the colonel hurts some of our feelings by remarking that the rear rank isn't very well dressed. But the purely military significance of the observation comes home to us eventually, and we shuffle humbly into place. He then restores our self-respect by a few words of, if not praise, at least tolerance, and passes down each rank handing us all a clip of cartridges. We have practised loading with dummy clips, but this is the real thing. Every man says a polite "thank you" as he takes his ammunition gingerly, and the colonel, giving the order to load, falls back cautiously on our right.

The wisdom of his move is made startingly clear almost at once, for the cartridges have no sooner clicked down into the magazines than the evening hush is rent by a deafening report. A rifle clatters down on my left, and from the direction of the main street comes a hoarse cry. The small eager man, anxious to be the quickest and smartest of us all, has inexplicably slipped a shell into the breech and pulled the trigger.

There is a second's awe-stricken pause. Then our ordered ranks are transformed into a galloping rabble, heading in the direction taken by the bullet. Debouching out of Pepper's Lane, the colonel bringing up the rear, we see that a small group has already gathered outside the establishment of Harry Bull. All are gesticulating towards the lettering over the window where the "u" of Harry's surname now has a neat round hole between its two uprights.

"Fall out!" bleats the colonel superfluously as he canters up to inspect the damage, and we straggle off towards our nearby headquarters, clustering excitedly round the hero of the evening, enlightening him as to how it happened.

As Harry Bull remarks to a number of admirers in the "Prince Regent" afterwards, it is "the only —— Bull some of them 'Ome Guardians is likely to get yet awhile."

2

Mainly about Beds

There are differing opinions amongst us about which duty is preferable—the Look-out on the Links or the Guard at Headquarters. (This is a handsome double-fronted shop ostensibly in the occupation of *Family* G. GADGER *Butcher*, so that the raw Local Defender is apt to think he has been misdirected until he sees the legend "L.D.V.H.Q." scratched on the blackened window.)

The Look-out is favoured by some on the grounds of excitement; in the early watches there is always the chance of being able to challenge elderly ladies who are taking their dogs for a walk and who might easily be parachutists in disguise but for the fact that the challenger has probably known them from early childhood—the challenger's early childhood, I mean. And in the late watches there is undoubtedly a better view of the air-raids, with added satisfaction to be got from standing fully exposed to splinters yet outside the jurisdiction of wardens.

But until to-night I personally have plumped for the Guard. There are more of us, and the atmosphere, though thicker, is more congenial (so much so that I have at times felt a vague surprise at not having been asked for my subscription)—and the

". . . able to challenge elderly ladies who are taking their dogs for a walk . . ."

Guard has to wear its uniforms only when it is turned out. This hasn't happened yet, but the general feeling is that it won't be long now.

However, the main thing about the Guard is that by taking the trouble to arrive five minutes early at H.Q. you have the choice of ten camp-beds, in varying degrees of desirability and repair.

At the Links, where the Look-out is only three strong (with two rifles and one bicycle), there is no choice at all, your bed being determined by the man who vacates it to relieve you at the watch, and who selects it to suit his own contours rather than yours. A bed upon which a fat man sleeps like a baby may bring to a thin one all the tortures of the rack.

So until to-night the Guard has had my vote; but to-night, as I lie gazing wide-eyed into the darkness I begin to wonder . . . .

Until midnight (when all but one of us yawned in concert and went to bed in Mr. Gadger's late bedrooms) the evening passed pleasantly enough. I won fourpence at rummy and performed an unusual feat at the dart-board, though I take no credit for this, as it was only made clear to me later. We had a good deal of harmless fun over a clip of dummy cartridges which had got lost and which eventually came to light in the magazine of our C/O.—a veteran of three years' Great War experience hitherto considered rather knowledgeable about guns. Also, I scored a personal triumph by being the only one to bring a flask of tea; the others were relying as usual on the supplies in Mr. Gadger's late shop-parlour, and these had unfortunately been exhausted by last night's Guard without a thought for the morrow. Something is going to be said about this, I understand. There was also some stale washing-up, and something will probably be said—though nothing done—about this too.

Yet I am uneasy in my mind. Is the acquisition of a bearable bed an infallible guarantee of a night's rest after all? My bed is more than bearable, it is luxurious—but I have not slept. It is free from all those unkindnesses planned by the manufacturers of camp-beds; it neither squeaks when I toss nor explodes when I turn; it lacks the conventional central strut to make excruciating contact with the spinal vertebrae; there are reasonably few naked tin-tacks to lacerate the sleeper's hands and tear holes in his socks; and (touch wood, which is easy) the entire contraption has not so far collapsed beneath me—a misfortune which has overtaken at least one member of the Guard each night since the Corps blossomed into being.

(On the early occasions of this disaster the muffled thud and rattle marking the bed's disintegration were followed alertly by cries of "Here they come!" and an unprincipled struggle for the nearest pair of uniform trousers. Now it evokes no more than the drowsy curses of the victim and the spiteful chuckles of the spared. Thus are we becoming inured to the rigours of war.)

There are four beds in our room, and we occupy them by reason of a lottery downstairs.

"*. . . handed them round at frequent intervals . . .*"

We are the night's four sentries. It is a new idea, and a commendable one, to segregate the watch in this way. Last time, when it was dotted indiscriminately over the whole building, an electric torch was flashed on each bed every two hours on the off-chance that it might contain the relieving sentry, and all ten of us passed an unsettled night.

Matters were made worse by one of our number's having armed himself against starvation with a bag of bull's-eyes. He was of a generous and wakeful disposition, and handed them round at frequent intervals until the grey light of dawn mercifully and unaccountably brought him sleep.

One of our beds is empty now, but two o'clock draws near; it will be filled then, and mine will be empty. I shall not be sorry when the footsteps lumber up the uncarpeted stairs, accompanied by the boom of a carelessly bouncing rifle-butt, for I have not slept yet.

The watch from ten to twelve was kept by a silent man with no collar. He stood apart, as sentries should, and watched our games of darts and dominoes with an air of detachment. He had not been with our Guard before, and none of us knew him, but he did not seem to mind this, nor inclined to remedy it. He was a very silent man, and seemed to be waiting for something other than an urgent summons shouted through our letter-box. I know now what he was waiting for.

Apart from saying to nobody in particular that he supposed we should get Lee-Enfields if we waited long enough, he spoke no word for three hours. He accepted a pipeful of tobacco from me at about 11.30, but that was the limit of our intimacy, and I rather think he forgot to thank me. He was a very silent man.

I held none of this against him, telling myself that his very presence amongst us was an earnest of his worth, that silence was known to be a virtue, and that collars were of small moment in times like these. But now—now that he sleeps within a few feet of me, I resent all these things: his presence amongst us, his silence (downstairs), and the laryngeal freedom afforded by his collarlessness. . . .

For the silent man is a King-snorer.

In this last two hours I have been subjected to such snoring as I hope I may never hear again. The technique is an odd one and worth recording.

The snore proper grows out of what seems at first to be merely inoffensive deep breathing; but with slow subtlety this changes to long, long sighs of ecstasy, as if his soul were filled with a delight which no words could paint. Then after a time comes a still longer but less joyous sigh. There is a note of pain in it, particularly in the falling cadences, which are fraught with bitterness and disillusionment, and this *motif* is developed ultimately to the stern exclusion of all joy. The note broadens into a sort of angry double-stopping, rising higher and higher in the tenor scale with each breath, till finally on a throbbing climax of anguish and despair it cracks and breaks into gibberish, richochetting down a hiccuping chromatic scale into a gobbling aftermath of remembered agony. A fit of dry coughing occurs at this point, and I know that full circle has been reached. The sleeper goes back to the *da capo* sign; the deep breathing begins again; then the joyous sighs; then the resentful note. . . .

Occasionally, just as it is coming to the boil, the occupant of the bed behind me ventures to move a limb, and the resulting succession of whip-crack effects interferes with the collarless man's machinery and sends the performance prematurely back to the double-bar. Otherwise there is no variation.

It was interesting at first. I sat up to listen to it. But after two hours it has palled, and now I lie down to listen to it. And through its familiar discords I strain my ears for the footsteps on the stairs. When they come I shall seize my rifle thankfully and hurry down below to get a bit of sleep.

3

Outward and Visible Signs

It was some time ago that little Mr. King startled us by shouting "They're 'ere!" from the doorway of H.Q. We were strolling to our eight o'clock parade, but this announcement quickened our heartbeats and our footsteps. We fought our way through the door towards the rifle-racks, our minds buzzing with remembered instructions to aim low and conserve our ammunition.

"Where?" we yelled ferociously.

"There!" answered little Mr. King, pointing.

It was just another anti-climax. He was only drawing our attention to the arrival of our denim overalls, lying on the floor in stiff mud-coloured bundles. As the excitement died out of us we noticed that Mr. King himself was strangely arrayed. "One each, there is," he said, restraining his admiration for the Ministry of Supply's scrupu lous impartiality—"but none of them don't fit me!"

This appeared to be only too true. Mr. King had

no hands and no feet. His waistline was but a few inches above his knees, and his neat stiff collar with the rounded wings of another age was exposed, frayed but gleaming, above a corrugated funnel of tunic-top.

"Never mind, King," said our Platoon Commander, emerging from the shadows with a battered cardboard box—"just come and sign for your buttons, will you? It may be better with the buttons." But Mr. King wagged his head doubtfully as he shuffled over to the table. "I dunno, I'm sure," he sighed, and searching a half-empty sleeve for his right hand he prepared to acknowledge receipt of twenty-three brown bone buttons and twenty-three little brass fasteners.

On top of our recent disappointment the uniforms fell a little flat with us all. They bore marks of hurried workmanship, and Mr. Punnitt, whose shop window up the street declares him to be a bespoke tailor, shook his head over them gravely. Hard words were spoken by our Section Leader, who found, after splitting his nails painfully for some minutes in a dark corner, that he had selected a tunic with dummy button-holes; and an argument between two junior members of "C" section as to whether the bottom of the tunic should go inside the top of the trousers, or vice versa, was developing promisingly by the time we emerged from the general scrimmage with two pieces of coarse cotton drilling each.

Most of us, evidently, came nearer to the manufacturers' conception of the human form than did Mr. King, though this must not be taken as a reflection upon that conscientious volunteer, but rather upon the rest of us. Tunics which were adequate in the sleeve seemed to run to seed at the waist, and trousers which all but fitted at the waist were wanting several inches in the leg. One or two of us who discovered one of each garment which fitted passably were later to find that their combination disclosed a hiatus of coloured shirt between the two.

In spite of all this, we were not ungrateful. Our armlets and forage-caps had promised small protection against the winds and rains to come, and the uniforms, even if they did smell of rancid linseed oil (arousing a vague nostalgia in those of us with cricketing pasts and a vague nausea in the remainder), would at least be "utilitarian." The newspapers had told us this, and for once we had to agree with them.

The evening's parade was one of mingled embarrassment and pride. We were embarrassed because the little boys ran after us, delightedly reading the sizes from the tickets on the backs of our trousers, and expressing pardonable surprise that Mr. King, at four feet ten, wore size nine-

". . . impossible to keep his rifle sloped and his trousers up . . ."

and-a-half, while Mr. Benn, the butcher (six feet tall and practically square), had chosen size three, medium. Our Section Leader was particularly embarrassed, because he found it impossible to keep his rifle sloped and his trousers up simultaneously; and Mr. Punnitt, conscious of being a bad advertisement, cast uncomfortable glances about him. And yet we were proud, though none of us would perhaps have admitted it; for we were wearing the King's uniform, even if it did fit our function rather than our physique.

All this, as I say, was some time ago. Three weeks at least. And since then we have been hearing disquieting tales of how other Companies have been magnificently equipped with greatcoats, service respirators, tin hats, belts, boots, bandoliers—everything, almost, from field marshals' batons downwards. We have been jealous of these lucky fellows. We have persecuted our Platoon Commander mercilessly. Were we not as deserving as the next village but one? Where were *our* coats? Where were *our* boots? How were *we* going to keep ourselves warm in the chill small hours? Why should the Great Preston chaps be swaggering about looking like real soldiers while we (for our pride was wearing off) bore a nearer resemblance to motor-mechanics out of a job?

Our Platoon Commander was patient, as Platoon Commanders have to be. He tried to placate us by offering a reward of five shillings for the first man to bring him Hitler's moustache dead or alive. But the men still murmured amongst themselves, one rebellious spirit even threatening resignation if he had to go on wearing his own boots; so he forsook humour for wisdom. "Never resign from anything," he counselled. "Stick to it and make yourself a damned nuisance till you get what you want. That's what I'm doing. Can I do more?"

As it happened there was no need to do more, because the other day when we turned up at H.Q. we were welcomed by a radiant Mr. King, swathed in khaki from head to foot. The great-coats had arrived. "One each!" said Mr. King, and added the unnecessary rider.

For our greatcoats we have nothing but praise. Thick, heavy, waisted, slant-pocketed, generous-skirted, they have made swashbucklers of us all. Mr. Willie Clarkson himself would not have scorned to have them in his wardrobe, and even that lesser sartorial authority, Mr. Punnitt, could scarce forbear to cheer. The younger ones amongst us, denim inadequacies concealed for ever, strut about their sentry-go with one eye on the country-side and the other closing in a permanent wink at the admiring village maidens.

Even Mr. King is not dissatisfied with his great-coat. Coming to his ankles as it does it puts mysterious inches on his height. His only anxiety is over the buttons, which are not the dull bone affairs which we had expected but highly polished brass. Knowing that their glory cannot endure, Mr. King is worried. "What are we going to do," he asked our Platoon Commander in premature despair—"when they goes all tarnished and dark? Then what are we going to do?"

". . . coming to his ankles as it does . . ."

"It's simple enough," said the Platoon Commander gently; "all you have to do is to send them to the War Office with a note saying 'Kindly clean and return.' "

Mr. King's face cleared a little, but he was still not easy in his mind.

"And what," he demanded, "do we use while they're away? It might take a week or more, with them as busy as they are."

4

Loss of Public Confidence

Our Section has had a humiliating experience this week. What its repercussions will be is a subject for nervous speculation amongst us. There is a sporting chance of course that the affair will never reach the ears of the authorities, but on the other hand the day may not be far off when our Section Leader is publicly deprived of his chevrons while we of the rank-and-file stand by in shame waiting for our buttons to be snipped off. Our destiny is in the hands of thirty-six civilians, any one of whom may be public-spirited enough to bring our military careers to an ignominious close; and although the passage of three uneventful days suggests that we may now be out of danger, it seems only wise to get our word in first. The true facts are accordingly presented here.

Monday's rain poured down our necks and Monday's gale rushed up the backs of our great-coats as we marched raggedly to our winter quarters at the Village Hall. Mr. Benn the butcher, leaning his vast frame into the wind and raising his voice above the tumult of the trees, observed that it was "a bit of an off-night for flat-bottomed boats," and little Mr. King, who had so much sail set that he could only tack doggedly in our rear, shrilled his agreement adding with some satisfaction, "Airyplanes neither!" These staunch volunteers spoke the thoughts of us all. We were in for a Quiet Night. Apart from two rather uncomfortable hours of vigil and five slightly less uncomfortable hours of fitful sleep, we could look forward to a fairly comfortable evening's rummy. Let it be stated boldly that our Section is comprised of ardent gamblers, and on Quiet Nights sums as large as threepence have been known to change hands.

(In case a false impression has been given in these chronicles it should be said that not all our nights are quiet. While not constituting what our talkative Mr. Corker would call a "stragetic objective" our village is nevertheless a popular spot for the "jettonizing" (to quote Mr. Corker again) of anything the *Luftwaffe* doesn't care to take back home. There is a theory of course that a long-derelict brickworks attracts attention, and some of our Company, after a two hours' watch in brilliant moonlight, have even felt that our sentry-box on the moor is over-conspicuous, but there is little evidence to support these views.)

As we panted up to the Hall, bristling with rifles, ammunition, field-dressings, anti-gas ointment, sandwiches, and vacuum flasks, our rising spirits were suddenly sent scuttling down to zero. For inside the railings there was gathered a great concourse of bicycles, male and female; male and female also were the many murmuring voices which floated out to us from behind the blackened windows, punctuated from time to time with hearty rustic laughter. Even as we listened in bewilderment there came the imperious jangling of a hand-bell, and the voices and laughter swelled suddenly to an uproar, through which could be heard the shuffle of many feet and the squeal of pushed-back chairs. As the voices died to a murmur again, Mr. Punnitt summed up the situation.

"Whist drive!" he exclaimed.

Mr. Corker snapped his fingers viciously and muttered to himself. Mr. King and Mr. Benn respectively declared that they would be blowed and would go to sea, and the rest of us turned to our Section Leader for guidance. Was there, we asked, any precedent for military procedure on finding the guard-room full of whist-playing civilians? Which was to come first, whist or war? Our Section Leader turned the problem over in his mind. Then he announced that we should have to go in.

The decision was received in silence. We were not without courage; we could face the invasion, endure bombardment, investigate shadows in the dead of night; but to file through the middle of a whist drive, laying ourselves open to the witticisms of those who knew us intimately in civil life, was more than we felt we could face. Mr. Corker was the first to find his voice.

"No!" he cried hoarsely, continuing with more respect—"What I mean to say, I mean to say——"

"Well, Mr. Corker?"

Despair brought Mr. Corker to the point in record time.

"My wife'll be in there!" he burst out—"I'll never 'ear the last of it!"

In the darkness one or two breaths were drawn in sharply, indicating that Mr. Corker's more personal problem was not his alone.

A patriotic reticence had forbidden us to disclose exactly how our spells of duty were occupied, but it was certain that feminine imagination had painted sombre pictures of hardships nobly borne, risks unflinchingly taken, fearful odds faced with a gallant smile—pictures, in short, which might be knocked sadly out of drawing by the spectacle of warrior-husbands gambling away the house-keeping money round a gas-fire. Clearly such tender illusions must be preserved at all costs. But how? The wind was blowing harder, the rain falling faster. Our hearts were filling with despair and our rifles with water when the voice of Mr. King was raised in sudden inspiration.

"There's a back door!" he squeaked—"on to the stage. There's curtains. I once sung 'ere!"

The fact that this last astounding revelation escaped comment speaks for the intensity of our welling relief. With one accord we surged in Mr. King's wake past the tangle of bicycles which leant against the side of the building, and presently ascended a short wooden stairway and slipped as silently as our equipment would allow through the providential back door on to a small and rickety platform. It was immediately obvious that need for caution was small. The sound of robustly-contested whist, though partially muffled by a pair of moth-eaten green velvet curtains which hid the players from view, would have drowned a far more boisterous counter-disturbance than we proposed to make. It seemed that with a little luck we should be able to enjoy our quiet night after all.

There was an old and dusty piano which proved an ideal rifle-rack, a stack of worm-eaten chairs, and a trestle-table supporting nothing but two vases of differing sizes but identically colourful design and two ragged brown paper parcels. These, with the exception of the large vase which we commandeered as an ash-tray (our usual soap-dish being difficult of access), we thrust under the piano with our haversacks, and when Mr. Tucker had been dispatched to take the first watch we unstacked half a dozen chairs and sat down with the feeling that treacherous waters had been skilfully navigated.

Looking back, it seems strange that not one of us had a premonition of what was to come. Though at that time of course none of us knew that it was Mr. Benn's birthday, a circumstance now held by some to be at the root of the whole trouble.

It was after the first game of rummy, when the cards lay scattered between us and the halfpennies had been assembled in neat but shallow piles at our elbows, that Mr. Benn, a little flushed in the face, solemnly produced from his haversack three pint beer-bottles. Our Section Leader, who rightly frowns on the mingling of alcohol and duty, gave the bottles a glance of sharp suspicion, and had actually opened his mouth for disciplinary reproof when Mr. Benn said with an apologetic smile that it was only cider. He then began to unwrap six thick tumblers from a piece of yellowed newspaper.

"Oh," said our Section Leader, temporarily at a loss—"well . . ."

"It's my birthday," said Mr. Benn simply—"fifty to-day."

"Oh, *well*," said our Section Leader, disarmed. And Mr. Benn was instantly overwhelmed with congratulations and with professions of incredulity that he should be a day over forty-five. Mr. Corker seized the opportunity to tell us his own age, that of his wife and his brother-in-law, and his brother-in-law's parents at the time of their death. He would have added still further to these details if Mr. Benn, now expanding fully, had not thrust a packet of small cigars under his nose, thus surprising him into silence.

"I *say*!" we said as we lit our cigars and tasted our cider and slackened our belts and unbuttoned our tunics.

"Well," said our Section Leader, with that touch

of nervousness common to proposers of toasts—"all the best, Mr. Benn!"

"All the best!" we echoed, springing to our feet and raising our glasses in the blue haze of Mr. Benn's cigars.

". . . 'all the best!' we echoed . . ."

"All the best," responded Mr. Benn, preparing to drink his own health enthusiastically—"and many of 'em!"

At this moment the now familiar hand-bell jangled beneath us with more than its usual vigour. At this moment, and upon this all too easily misconstrued tableau, the Master of Ceremonies drew back the moth-eaten green velvet curtains and, with a confidence born of careful stage-management, took away our ash-tray.

"The first prize for ladies," he declaimed in the awful hush which had fallen amongst the nine whist tables, "goes to Mrs. Corker . . ."

". . . snatched up his rifle and disappeared into the night . . ."

Conscious that something was wrong, he wheeled round and noticed us. He then dropped the first prize for ladies. An apple-core bounced amongst the splintered remains. There was a silence that could be felt. It was broken by the prize-winner.

"Fred!" cried Mrs. Corker.

"Well, well," said a fat man at the far end of the room. "The 'Ome Guard at work!"

"Oh, my lor!" groaned Mr. Corker, and like a rushing mighty wind snatched up his rifle and disappeared into the night, presumably to relieve Mr. Tucker half an hour before his time. In his flight he dislodged our table-top, which cascaded its load of playing-cards, cigarette-packets, coppers and beer-bottles about our petrified feet.

Later, our Section Leader placed the simple facts before the Master of Ceremonies. Mr. King and Mr. Punnitt have since placed them before Mrs. King and Mrs. Punnitt, who were present playing as gentlemen; and no doubt Mr. Corker has emphasized to Mrs. Corker the distinction between beer and cider, between a brawl and a birthday. Our only remaining anxiety, as I said at the beginning, is whether any of those whist players will place the facts before our Platoon Commander—and what sort of a hand we shall hold if they do.

5

To Meet the General

It was sprung on us suddenly, as these things so often are—a General Inspection of the whole battalion of us on Sunday morning at 10.15.

We were on duty on the Friday night and our Section Leader broke the news to us with a nice mingling of apprehension and dignity, using the voice he keeps for keying us up to ordeals outside our normal routine, and affecting not to read in our guileless faces the emotions of a Section that had been sunk without warning. For we had less than two days' notice to get the dubbing off our boots, the suspicion of green off our buttons—and to learn how to present arms. It was not, we felt, long enough.

The instructions which our Section Leader read to us were in unfamiliar English. There was much said on the subject of "embussing" and "debussing" —terms which baffled us for a time until little Mr. King, with shrill inspiration, construed them to mean "gettin' in and out of the chara." (We were to be carried off in real Army lorries, with real Army camouflage and real Army drivers; it was this last amenity which decided the motorists of our Section to take their own cars, offering their spare seats to the rest of us.)

But at least the author of the document had left nothing to chance. It was all there—when we were to start, where we were to go, what we were to do when we got there, and what we were to wear to do it in. The hope was even expressed that every man would be home in time for his dinner, and although this point caused some whispered speculation on whether the midday or the evening meal was meant, it was left to a sardonic member of "A" Section to remark on the Sunday (after we had been standing at ease and apparently forgotten for an hour and a half) that the instructions had failed to mention which *day*.

It would be untrue to say that the prospect of the Inspection threw us into a panic—even the big bomb that irreverently blew the windows out of our late Headquarters didn't do that—but we were seized by a general nervousness; even before the last ungrammatical cadences of the instructions had died away many of us were surreptitiously sloping and ordering our arms in various corners of the room, and finally Mr. Punnit and Mr. Tucker, practising halting with their gaze fixed intently on their boots, came into collision with such a deafening crash of equipment that our Section Leader had to call us peremptorily to order. He soon saw, however, that our unco-ordinated antics were directed only towards preserving the Section's fair name and, smoothing out the typescript gravely, he herded us into one of Headquarters' larger rooms to put us through our paces in something approaching unanimity.

"Does a battalion," asked little Mr. King, ever anxious to learn, "mean Arthur Smith's lot, and Jim and Joe Cooper's gang, and the Little Cumpton crowd that sleeps in Pinfold's garage?" Mr. Benn, the only one of us too near to Mr. King to pretend not to have heard the question, said guardedly that he supposed so, and busied himself with the adjustment of his rifle-sling. Mr. King was not entirely satisfied, and put the question to our Section Leader as soon as we were assembled in the big room. He, his attention only partly distracted from the matter in hand, said that it meant everybody.

Mr. King was incredulous. "Why," he exclaimed, "there'd never be room enough, not on Parker's

Plain—not for the whole million an' a half of us!"

So our Section Leader had to explain after all, and did so very skilfully, considering all things, accepting Mr. Corker's respectful but voluble corrections from time to time with good grace. He concluded stirringly by saying that all we need worry about was our immediate task of being the smartest Section in the smartest Platoon in the smartest Company in the Battalion. So, much moved, we formed ranks, a little surprised to find that there were only five of us (Mr. Curtis being out on sentry-go), but filling up the blank files with two chairs and a coal-bucket and squaring our shoulders determinedly.

The details of the drill, kindly supplied in the instructions, were read over to us twice, while we nodded with every appearance of comprehension and made tentative little movements with our feet and our rifles.

"Now then," said our Section Leader at last—"are we all ready?"

There were five non-committal grunts and a little shuffling.

"Open order . . . *march!*"

The room was really not big enough. Mr.

Corker's two forward paces caused him to bury his face against our Section Leader's shoulder, and Mr. Benn, stepping out heavily an appreciable moment later, drawn up to his full height of six feet two, passed his rifle-muzzle through the gas-

"*. . . his second pace wedging his right boot in the coal bucket . . .*"

globe with a ringing report and plunged the rehearsal into darkness and confusion. Inevitably, little Mr. King marched forward instead of back, his second pace wedging his right boot in the coal-bucket, and as the rest of us floundered painfully amongst what seemed at least a dozen chairs, a dark-blue flame hissed us contemptuously from the demolished fitting over our heads.

It was decided after this that it would perhaps be as well to parade a few minutes early on Sunday morning and have our rehearsal then. . . .

To the reader who already suspects that we disgraced ourselves shamefully in the eyes of the General, let it be said at once that we did nothing of the kind. We acquitted ourselves admirably at the actual performance. Our appearance, our drill, our general air of keenness and potential gallantry were all beyond reproach. We know this, because the General told us so himself, very hoarsely, and from a great way off, and it warmed our hearts—which was a good thing, because it had been a very cold morning.

The Army lorries which were to take our Platoon to Parker's Plain arrived half an hour late. This, though lowering our opinion of the Army, to whose pitch of efficiency we are constantly being urged to aspire, at least gave us time to polish up our drill, thus delighting our Section Leader and the small number of villagers abroad at that hour. Although our Section was to travel under its own power we felt it would be unkind to set out before the transport for the rest of the Platoon was available, so that it was nearly 10.45 when we "debussed" at the Plain. This sweep of sloping grass-land, but for two embittered-looking regulars with a Bren gun, and an elderly gentleman in rim-less spectacles and immaculately creased denims, was empty. We were late, but almost all the rest of the battalion was later.

The elderly gentleman, who looked worried and wore his forage-cap at an angle of precisely ninety degrees, buttonholed Mr. Punnitt as soon as he got out of his car and asked him what Company he belonged to. Mr. Punnitt, after hesitating a moment, handed the inquirer over to our Section Leader, who surprised us by adopting a deeply respectful demeanour, the elderly gentleman being none other than our Company Commander, grow-ing a little concerned about his absentee Company.

It was another half-hour before anything else happened, and by this time we were dancing with the cold. The sky was frosty-blue, and a thin icy wind tweaked our noses and pinched our ears. There seemed nothing for us to do, yet we feared to go far away, feeling that the rest of the battalion might sweep into view at any moment. Eventually it did, platoon by platoon, company by company, hundreds and hundreds of marching men, all an hour late but looking, as even the lethargic Mr.

Benn was moved to exclaim, "good for half a dozen Adolfs each." We were concerned, however, for two reasons; first, because all these contingents were wearing their pigskin gaiters, which we, although newly issued with ours, had been forbidden by our instructions to wear, and secondly because so far only three of our platoons had turned up. As the other companies passed us, mounted the slope and formed themselves into neatly spaced ranks in the distance, our Company Commander looked increasingly troubled and took out his big silver watch more and more frequently.

By this time we had given up any hope of keeping warm. It was never explained to us why we were so early, or why everyone else was so late, nor did we ever discover why we were not put through a few circulation-promoting exercises instead of being allowed to stand about devising new ways of holding our rifles. On the first count we ultimately contented ourselves with a vague theory that the trouble was something to do with Summer-time, and on the second—well no one put into words the suspicion that our Company Commander had misgivings about showing us off to rival Commanders before it was absolutely necessary.

It was just as we had resigned ourselves to death

from exposure that a flushed messenger arrived with the news that as no Army transport had called to collect our other five platoons their Commanders presented their compliments and regretted that they would be unable to attend the Inspection.

We did not catch what our Company Commander said, but it was with some terseness that he fell us in and marched us up to the top of the hill. Our opinion of the Army dropped several more points.

After that the affair was more or less over. We dressed ranks, we opened and closed them, we sprang to attention, a tall figure strode past us, we heard those warm words of praise, accepted good wishes for our winter training, "embussed" and went home in time for dinner.

For some reason or other we were all very pleased with ourselves, possibly because, unlike the Army, none of us had let anybody down, possibly because—again unlike the Army—we have up our sleeves the comforting thought that we can always give Sir Edward Grigg a fortnight's notice if we feel like it. Not of course that any of us do. . . .

6

Taking the Chill Off

The whole of our Platoon has its greatcoats now —even Mr. Benn the butcher, whose "measures," as little Mr. King would say, must have caused quite a stir in the Gents' Out-size Department at the Ministry of Supply. Mr. Benn's coat would make two of Mr. King's and at least one and a half of everybody else's, and it is still a little tight across the front.

But greatcoats are not enough. The nights are growing cold and the winds whistle freely over the open spaces; the frost steals upon us in the small hours, and even behind his greatcoat-collar the teeth of the sentry can be heard chattering in the darkness.

Recognizing these things, Mr. Anthony Eden (or was it Sir Edward Grigg?) has promised us uniforms of khaki serge, just like the real soldiers wear, and appreciation of this kindly thought has been voiced on all sides; our denim overalls, so recently our joy and pride, can scarcely be called weather-resisting, and their mysterious redolence of linseed oil seems to hang over us like a pall. But there has also been voiced, by thinking Volunteers, a suspicion that these luxury garments may only arrive with the warmer weather of 1941—a suspicion which casts no slur on the integrity of Mr. Anthony Eden (or Sir Edward Grigg), but arises only from trifling disappointments of the past and from a consciousness that Government contractors are pressed for time these days.

At any rate, we of ''B'' Section have decided to use our own initiative in keeping the weather at bay, and a week or two ago Mr. King, who had repeatedly declared himself to be "cold as a frog," gave us a lead by parading in a heavy felt hat instead of his forage cap. (We had not then discovered that our caps embodied an ingenious machinery for turning them into ear- and neck-protectors.) On his hands he wore light-grey mittens, and the removal of his greatcoat disclosed a long orange pullover. Some of this was hidden by his tunic, but most of it made a splash of cheerful colour below it.

The notably small crop of witticisms which greeted this costume showed that the rest of us recognized wisdom when we saw it, and the next day our wives had to face persuasive propaganda designed to prove that knitting for the Forces and knitting for the Home Guard were equally vital contributions to the national effort. It was without qualms of conscience that we saw scarves, socks and gloves originally intended for deserving strangers diverted to our own throats, feet and fingers.

Khaki has very properly been the prevailing shade of these labours of love, although Mr. King's move towards brighter duty-nights has been supported by some. Mr. Punnitt, for instance, has taken to a red flannel waistcoat of old-world design, and Mr. Corker has paraded of late looking disconcertingly Plantagenet in a Balaclava helmet of Air Force blue. From the facial aperture this helmet seems to have been intended for a smaller man, and it is only by careful adjustment that Mr. Corker can simultaneously speak and see. If it works too far up his conversation becomes a woollen drone; too far down, and he is as blind as a bat. We have yet to learn how this will affect his sighting and challenging of the enemy on a frosty night.

But to keep ourselves warm for two hours on the wind-swept moor is only half our problem. The other half is to keep ourselves warm in the gusty and rarefied air of the Village Hall, where the floor-boards rise and fall gently on the bosom of the breeze and the canvas of our camp-beds has actually been seen to flap. Outside we can march, run, leap in the air, clap our hands together or even rehearse our arms drill; on clear nights we

". . . as blind as a bat . . ."

can keep our circulation going by practising swift dives into a shallow adjacent trench, just in case the droning overhead should be supplemented by an approaching swishing sound. Inside, the problem is more acute. Lying on our beds, the fever of hardly-contested rummy rapidly cooling in our veins, there is little we can do to shake off the icy hand which seizes us in the small of the back and slowly turns us to marble from top to toe.

To a certain extent Mr. Punnitt has improved things by introducing the "Punnitt System" of bed-making. Basically this consists of making one blanket do the work of two, and we all displayed interest in it from the first; strangely enough, however, none of us has been able quite to get the hang of it, so that Mr. Punnitt (who is perhaps kind-hearted rather than gullible) regularly gives each of us a further demonstration of his ingenuity and skill. "Mr. Punnitt!" cries Mr. Tucker, who is smoking by the gas-fire—"I can't get my blankets right!" And Mr. Punnitt, untangling blankets at the far end of the Hall, says that he will come and have a look when he has finished Mr. Benn's. (Mr. Benn is sitting beside Mr. Tucker, reading the paper.) Altogether, Mr. Punnitt is one of the most popular men in the Section.

Incidentally, coming across a piece of Government literature the other night at H.Q., we found that we were supposed to be issued with one blanket to two men. As our present quota is five blankets each, we feel that there must have been a slip somewhere, though it was only the more conscientious of us who wondered for a moment whether this should be pointed out to the authorities. Perhaps we have extra blankets in place of tin hats, belts, bayonets and those rather foppish shoulder flashes affected by some Companies. Our blankets are amongst the Platoon's most

". . . a good homely smell . . ."

treasured equipment, in spite of a certain indefinable odour attaching to them. Our Section Leader, remarking one night upon this odour, was told by our Platoon Commander (who seeks to make the best of everything) that it was a good homely smell. Our Section Leader replied, with great respect, that it depended on what sort of a home you came from. . . .

Hot drinks, of course, have been part of each man's personal equipment all along—even in the comparatively oppressive nights of summer, and but for an unfortunate experience of little Mr. King's it is probable that hot bottles would also have become the order of the night. Mr. King, whose orange pullover had helped to keep him warm on sentry-go, still remained "cold as a frog" in his bed. He paraded one night, therefore, with two vacuum flasks instead of one, and a rubber hot-water bottle rolled up in his greatcoat pocket. Coming in from his watch at three in the morning, he filled his hot-water bottle with steaming cocoa, thrust it down his blankets, and sat on the edge of his bed to enjoy a cupful of scalding and somewhat brackish hot water.

The incident made less of an impression on Mr. King than on the rest of us, and it was only while we were packing the beds away next morning that he referred to it casually.

"But what," we asked, "will Mrs. King say when she finds her hot-water bottle full of cocoa?"

"She won't," replied Mr. King briskly—"I've just drunk it!"

He added that he felt "warm as a pudding."

7

Recrudescence of Mistrust

Encouraged by several cautionary remarks in high quarters designed to keep us on our guard against wolves in sheep's clothing, there has been a marked revival amongst us of hawk-eyed watchfulness and easily-aroused suspicion. The final edge was put on our vigilance last week when a regular sergeant delivered to us a lecture on "Sentries and Patrols." Home Guards as a body—this was the burden of his song—were too apt to regard mankind as a friendly species, too prone to accept a familiar uniform as a guarantee of its occupant's *bona fides*, too diffident in insisting on proofs of identity, and far too loose in interpreting the ". . . or I fire" clause in the ritual of the sentry's challenge. Everybody, we gathered, was a suspect unless otherwise proved, and when the lecture was over we accorded the sergeant a hearty vote of thanks and with difficulty suppressed an impulse to accuse him of being German Intelligence in disguise.

Mr. Benn and little Mr. King, marching down to the Village Hall half an hour later, at ease and out of step, had clearly taken the matter deeply to heart. It was only after close scrutiny, for example, that P.C. Hooper, hailing them amiably as he went on his nightly way, was accorded the usual "Now then, Joe"; and in the weighty conversation which lasted them until they reached their destination not even the village's oldest-established tradesmen escaped calumny. Mr. Benn's suspicions were also directed against our newly-appointed postman, and were mainly founded on his having two arms, whereas his predecessor had had only one; and Mr. King, wagging a shrewd head, made out a strong case against Miss Witterick, the District Nurse.

That night Mr. Tucker and Mr. Punnitt, who relieved Mr. King and Mr. Benn respectively on sentry-go, were lucky to escape with their lives.

It has always been our custom for the man on duty to challenge his approaching relief, but up to now this has been a rather informal business. We can all recognize each other's welcome footsteps, and while Mr. Corker is almost certain to come on duty singing "I'm dancing with tears in my eyes," it is also generally established that Mr. Curtis will be whistling "Alice Blue Gown"; Mr. Punnitt usually blows his nose with a trumpeting sound en route to the sentry-box, and Mr. Tucker can awaysl be heard coming at the double to get his circulation up. These personal idiosyncrasies have been enough in the past.

So it was a surprise to Mr. Tucker, trotting rhythmically through the night, to hear an unwonted asperity in Mr. King's shrill "Halt!—'oo goes there?"

"It's me," shouted Mr. Tucker, still trotting—"why?"

"Never mind why," replied the intrepid Mr. King, not entirely according to Regulations—"I've took my safety-catch off!"

At this Mr. Tucker slowed down to a walk, and when Mr. King, still not satisfied, announced firmly that he proposed to fire he came to an abrupt standstill.

"What's the matter, Mr. King?" asked Mr. Tucker, mildly uneasy—"it's me—Mr. Tucker."

There was a pause. Mr. King could be seen dimly in the gloom, apparently going systematically through his pockets, muttering under his breath. After some seconds he abandoned the search with an exclamation of annoyance.

"Could you lend me your flashlight, Mr. Tucker?" he asked, a new note of humility in his voice; and stepping forward to receive it he shone it in Mr. Tucker's face for a moment. Then:

"Pass, friend!" he said, and went on to ease the situation by complaining that he was as cold as a toad.

Four hours later, when Mr. Punnitt marched briskly forth, blowing his nose as penetratingly as ever, the bellow of Mr. Benn's challenge rattled the windows within a quarter of a mile radius. Mr. Punnitt, thinking it merely a piece of ill-timed fun, didn't even trouble to respond.

"*Halt, or I fire!*" roared Mr. Benn again, and even then Mr. Punnitt failed to grasp the gravity of the situation. It was the menacing rattle of a rifle-bolt that finally brought things home to him.

Pulling up in his tracks he hurriedly proclaimed his identity, adding an agonized injunction to Mr. Benn to "point that thing in the air!" During the subsequent brief deadlock Mr. Benn was not blessed with any inspiration about a flashlight, but presently an equally ingenious idea was vouchsafed him.

"Mr. Punnitt?" he asked, making sure of his ground.

''I told you, didn't I?'' said Mr. Punnitt.

"What's your rifle number?" demanded Mr. Benn triumphantly.

Mr. Punnitt had not the least idea, but his presence of mind saved him.

"Two-four-oh-seven-three-nine-three-four-one-eight," he gabbled with entirely unfounded conviction.

"Pass, Mr. Punnitt," said Mr. Benn, looming up hugely—"All quiet, except for Jim Archer's ruddy ducks!"

It was the praiseworthy attention to duty of these two Volunteers which earned for them the distinction of inaugurating a new duty-night ritual this week. Two of us were to carry out a "dusk patrol," and our Section Leader, reports of Mr. King's and Mr. Benn's unbudgeable integrity having come to his ears, detailed the pair of them to scour the immediate countryside for undesirable aliens during the hour preceding our usual time of parade.

Three hours after their departure upon this expedition there was still no sign of their return. Brows were furrowed, heads were shaken gravely, and our Section Leader was on the point of raising volunteers for a search-party when the missing men shambled shamefacedly in, looking very warm in spite of the coldness of the night, and smelling faintly of beer. Piecing together their somewhat scrappy stories and filling in the blanks from our knowledge of most of the parties concerned, we were eventually able to gather some idea of how they had been delayed.

In their new-found zeal Mr. Benn and Mr. King had decided to include in their itinerary a small wood which, though not actually on their prescribed route, seemed a likely spot for ill-disposed strangers to lie in hiding. The light was failing fast, so that when Mr. King first thought he spied the figure of a man in the lower branches of a fir-tree he hesitated to call Mr. Benn's attention to it. After a few more paces, however, there could no longer be any doubt, and he seized his colleague's hairy wrist in an excited grip. "Lie down!" he urged hoarsely, and suited the action to the word by falling flat amongst the wet pine-needles. Mr. Benn boomingly demanded "Why?" but followed suit nevertheless. Mr. King pointed to the fir-tree. "There's a man in it," he explained.

"By cheese!" said Mr. Benn, after a moment—"and there is, too!"

Thus agreed on the existence of a quarry, Volunteers Benn and King began to stalk it. They crawled as far as the tree-trunk without being observed, and even then (so they said) it was only the faint click of their safety-catches being thumbed forward that gave them away. To their relief the man up the tree was the first to speak. They themselves would have been at a loss for the apt phrase, since it seemed foolish to order a man in a tree to halt, or even to say "Who goes there?" to a person obviously going nowhere.

"Hey!" said the man in the tree, looking down the muzzles of two American Lee-Enfields (for the stalkers had risen to their feet), "what's the blinking game, eh?"

He thrust an arm down to part the branches, revealing a khaki sleeve whose two suspiciously clean-looking stripes shone opalescently in the dim light.

"Don't you move!" cried Mr. King sharply, rattling a cartridge into the breech.

"What do you reckon you're doing up there?" demanded Mr. Benn, doing likewise.

"Minding my own business," said the man— "that's more than you are—Mutt and Jeff!"

"I'll give you Mutt and Jeff!" said Mr. Benn, stung. "Come down out of that!''"

Grinning, the man came down. To an uncritical eye he would have appeared to be a regular corporal. As he reached the ground he peered closely at the inscription on Mr. King's right arm and made a noise signifying his amused comprehension.

"*. . . that's more than you are— Mutt and Jeff*"

Volunteers Benn and King were annoyed at their captive's attitude. True, he appeared harmless, if disrespectful, but was not this the type, after all, against whom the Sergeant's lecture had warned them? Mr. King, with a bright thought, stepped forward and relieved the corporal of his rifle. At this the grin vanished.

"Here, steady on!" said the prisoner, making as

if to snatch the weapon back. But Mr. Benn pushed his own rifle against the man's third button.

"Who do you reckon you are?" he inquired sternly.

The corporal's first impulse was obviously not to answer, but a glance at the two hawklike faces made him change his mind.

"Corporal Frederick John Hickmott," he said grudgingly, adding his unit.

"'Dentity Card?" said Mr. King, holding out his hand as to the manner born.

The corporal put a hand in his left breast-pocket; and there it stayed for some seconds, while his grin, which had shown signs of returning life, died suddenly.

"Cor!" said the corporal in an awed whisper—"must have lost it, crawling about in this —— spinney!"

Mr. Benn and Mr. King exchanged knowing nods. If a man discovered up a tree, claiming to be a British corporal and unable to prove his identity, wasn't a wolf in sheep's clothing, then what was?"

"I think," said Mr. Benn, with quiet authority "—you'd better come along with us. 'Bout *turn!*"

Protesting loudly, the corporal about turned and the procession moved off through the trees.

The police station, where it had been decided to take the prisoner, was two miles along the main road. Only half this distance had been covered when he suddenly declared himself to be ill and in need of brandy. While this well-tried ruse did not deceive his captors for a moment it did seem to them an opportunity to demonstrate how our prisoners of war are treated, and it was fortunate that the party was at that moment opposite the front door of "The Angel," a small inn well known to Volunteers Benn and King.

It was early, and the private bar was empty as yet, save for the landlord, who, having greeted Mr. Benn with "Now then, Hubert," and Mr. King with "Now then, Arthur," astounded them both by greeting the corporal with "Now then, Freddie, my boy; are you standing the 'Ome Guard treat, then?"

"Here!" protested Mr. Benn, outraged—"do you know 'im, then?"

"Know 'im!" chuckled the landlord—"why, he's my brother Fred's boy. Down at Blitchford Camp, aren't you, Freddie?"

"That's right," said Corporal Hickmott, the

grin returning sevenfold—"and mine's a bitter. Thanks, old cock," he added to Mr. King, "for carrying my rifle!"

Our Section Leader, when the tale was told, said he could see that it was only fair to buy the prisoner a drink in the circumstances, but he did feel that Volunteers Benn and King had taken more time over it than was really necessary.

"Ah!" said little Mr. King—"but 'e remembered—see?—as he'd left his Section lying in a ditch awaiting orders. We 'ad to go back and help him find 'em, see?"

Our Section Leader said Yes, he saw. . . .

8

Winter Quarters

We have taken a bungalow.

In the summer, it may be remembered, we took the late Mr. Gadger's butcher's shop, and later on the Lady Members' Rest Room in the Club-house; autumn saw us successively in the Schools (by kind permission of the County Education Committee), the British Legion Hut, and the Village Hall of icy memory. For the winter we have taken a dear little bungalow.

But perhaps this is a misstatement. It cannot be very dear or we should never have taken it. As a matter of fact it is not yet certain whether it has been taken by us or by Sir Edward Grigg on our behalf; at our own suggestion we are giving over the sum of sixpence a night out of our pay (or subsistence allowance, as some like to call it), but whether this is for rent, or merely rates, lighting, heating and cleaning is not really known.

Nor, remembering how easily we kept getting lost in it last night, can it justly be called little.

It has two or three rec., at least two bed., with kitch., bath and a garden full of awkwardly-placed trees thrown in.

Our bungalow is called "Elle Vue," a piece of bad French due to a bit of the front gate having

"*. . . standing in their bare feet . . .*"

been at some time wrenched away and lost, together with the complementary letter "B." However, it is useful to be able to read even "Elle Vue" by the discreet light of our torches, as this prevents confusion with the bungalow next door, which is built to an exactly similar pattern, but is called "Peacehaven." It was only towards the end of our first spell of duty that this useful tip was called to our notice by the residents at "Peacehaven," who said, standing in their bare feet, that while they had no objection to our bawling and tramping outside their gate all night if it meant winning the war, they felt bound to draw the line at being got out of bed every hour and a half to explain why the catch was down on their front door.

There is no luxury at "Elle Vue." The furnishings are sparse, consisting of an unresilient horse-hair sofa of unknown (or unconfessed) ownership, ten camp-beds (three of them incurably maimed), a large gardening-basket full of chipped cups, and a quantity of small cardboard boxes which, in the absence of our usual soap-dish, we used as ash-trays (for one performance only). There are no pictures on the walls—yet; the only mural decoration is the green baize notice-board transferred from H.Q. (which is itself to be transferred shortly, into our second-best bedroom). The notice-board bears sheaves of mimeographed announcements with such headings as "How to Clean Your Rifles," "Bicycles and Respirators," "Common German Phrases" and "Tactical Exercises, July 12th, 1940." There is also a moving appeal in faded handwriting, requesting that a pair of blue braces, if found, should be returned to H. Tuffin of "D" Section.

The design of the bungalow confused us a little at first, and it may be some time yet before we can feel sure of making our way successfully to whatever part of the house we set out for. The original owner, we imagine, must have had second thoughts about the place after he had built it—or perhaps a subsequent owner didn't much care for the original owner's first thoughts. Whatever the cause, structural alterations have certainly been carried out and have resulted chiefly in an astonishing number of doors. The building is riddled with them, each room having at least three, and the house itself about half a dozen leading out into obscure corners of the garden, where ropes of creeper lie in wait to trip up the unwary, and sentinel trees lurk at every threshold to clump him over the head.

This multiplicity of exits and entrances was the cause of some delay in our settling down for the night. Mr. King, scuttling to and fro in a sort of first-day-of-term excitement, would rush a camp-bed out of a room by one door and at once bring it back by another, where he would set it up briskly in the corner from which he had just removed it, fully believing that he had taken it over to the far side of the house.

As we were all working with the same zest as Mr. King, the general effect was one of a sudden and unaccountable increase in our numbers. Mr. Benn, Mr. Punnitt and Mr. Tucker, for instance, would no sooner leave the second best bedroom through one wall in search of blankets than they would troop in again through the wall adjoining; at the same time Mr. Curtis and Mr. Corker would be carrying out the reverse manœuvre, so that when our Section Leader glanced up thoughtfully from his Orders of the Day he would be staggered to see nothing less than a March Past taking place before his very eyes. At one stage he began to count us quietly, but upon reaching the early twenties he passed a hand across his brow and went outside for a breath of air, wondering, no doubt, how on earth he was to make our six rifles go round.

Mr. Corker, whose civil occupation of A.A. patrolman equips him to deal with matters of this kind, ultimately established some semblance of order by labelling various doors "IN" and "OUT," and locking up the remainder.

There are many points in favour of "Elle Vue."

We are self-contained there, for one thing; we do not feel that the seat of our activities by night is given over by day to golfers, school-children and the like. The place is ours entirely, save of course for the Platoon's other five Sections, whose claims we are bound to recognize, if only with a slightly patronizing tolerance.

We have gas, we have water, and we are to have the telephone if the Post Office can be persuaded to put it in; we have a permanent black-out, not requiring to be augmented by greatcoats, as was the case at the Schools, nor propped up by a Browning repeating rifle and a broom-handle, like the one at the Village Hall; it was even suggested that we should have a resident charlady, though this scheme was dropped on the grounds of that rigid propriety which governs us, as gentlemen if not officers, at all times. But our immediate joy in "Elle Vue" is because of its facilities for seasonable though suitably restrained celebrations on Christmas Day next, on which isolated public holiday our Section will, the calendar tells us, be on duty. This prospect, now that we have a home of our own, is viewed with surprising fortitude. The more imaginative of us have even foreseen the festooning of the walls with gay streamers and the pleasing spectacle of our Section Leader, improperly dressed in a yellow paper hat, democratically pulling crackers with his men. Christmas in the Club-house, the Schools, or the Village Hall —that would have been a melancholy affair; in

". . . democratically pulling crackers with his men . . ."

the bungalow we shall be able, with any luck, to keep it merry still.

But where there are pros, there must inevitably be cons. The main con about "Elle Vue"—always supposing that we shall learn to find our way about the place, and not try to leave the garden by the back fence instead of the front gate—is that it is far removed from that piece of moorland which it is our privilege to guard. Neither the violent sounding of our ship's bell, hanging as it always does on the sentry-box nail, nor the firing of the sentry's rifle (or, indeed, anybody else's), nor the sounds of a struggle, nor the harsh gutturals we have been told to expect from the unfriendly —none of these noises could possibly carry from our solitary look-out to any of the rooms in our bungalow. This means that we are obliged to dispatch a lone patrol every ten minutes to see that the sentry is still there. All reports were favourable last night, which was a night of rain and gale, but the point was raised as to what the lone patrol should do in the event of the sentry having disappeared—a point which has not yet been cleared up.

It is felt, particularly by sentries just off duty, that something should be done about the establishing of communications between the moor and "Elle Vue," although it is generally doubted whether a satisfactory scheme can be worked out. If the difficulties prove insurmountable then, as our Section Leader said in his unruffled way, we shall have to guard a different bit of moor in future, that's all.

9

A Jerk in it

In the past, except for a number of uplifting pamphlets and a single thrilling glimpse of an inspecting General, we have not come very much under the spell of the Army proper. We have copied the way it wears its caps and slings its rifles, and we have puzzled over its knack of getting that neat overlap in its trousers below the knee, but these are superficialities unlikely to lead to any deeper understanding. Recently, however, thanks to the zeal of an ambitious few, more intimate relations have been established between our two forces.

The liaison had its beginnings in the cordial atmosphere of a public-house a few miles distant, much frequented by real soldiers. It was there that a keen member of "D" Section became friendly, towards the end of the evening, with no less a personage than a Sergeant-major. It transpired that this Sergeant-major would condescend, if asked nicely, to give our Platoon a hint or two about winning the war, and the news was hurried home to our Section Leaders, who lost no time in putting negotiations in train.

When we of the rank-and-file heard of this windfall we were flattered and a little touched to think that a busy warrior, with many calls on his time and temper, should be willing to squander the one and risk total loss of the other, with nothing as his reward but a promise of free transport both ways; and when it became known that our Platoon was only one of several benefiting from his lofty altruism, our admiration for the man soared giddily. This was the spirit, we said to ourselves, that was going to whack the Axis.

However, when our Section Leader asked him on his first visit how on earth he found time to do so much for so many, he replied with a slight air of surprise that he had nothing else to do; was, in fact, attached to the Home Guard officially. This revelation exploded our theories about his lovable nature, but compensated us to a certain extent by swelling our self-esteem. To have a real Sergeant-major attached to us seemed to place us on a higher level altogether, even if the attachment had proved to be official rather than emotional.

It must be admitted that when he eventually stood before us we felt a vague chill of disappointment to find that this was not the Sergeant-major famed in song and story. Here was no fifteen-stone despot with purple complexion, spiky moustache

"... *hurling himself like lightning to the ground* ..."

and violent tongue, but a small pale man with smouldering dark eyes and considerable etymological restraint.

We soon learned that his stock-in-trade, in addition to an undoubted grasp of his subject, included a small fund of mild witticisms delivered with no apparent expectancy of applause, and a disconcerting habit of hurling himself like lightning to the ground in order to demonstrate any point that might not be quite clear. His diction displayed that inability to cope successfully with the letter "t" which has done so much to enhance the popularity of Mr. Jack Warner. "Pu' a jerk in i'!" he pleaded, towards the end of his first Sunday morning with us in the Village Hall. "My dinner's all poured ou'!"

This is one of his favourite jests; another, and one which we shall not easily tire of hearing, is to beseech us not to look so worried, as we "ain't doin' i' for a livin'." And this is perhaps the secret of his tolerance towards us. As raw recruits who had accepted the King's shilling instead of Sir Edward Grigg's one-and-sixpence, we should probably have been bullied to death in the first five minutes, but the authorities have obviously told him that we are a touchy lot, entitled to quit in a huff if we feel like it, and have warned him not to provoke us into indulging this valued privilege.

It speaks well for us—or perhaps for some subtle magnetism in him—that we do not take advantage of his gentleness to treat him with anything but deep respect. Even if he does fall a little short of our conception of sergeant-majors as a body, the tradition hallowing his rank forbids that easy familiarity which we adopt towards our own superior officers. Some of the more impressionable of us even address him humbly as "Sir," and a member of "A" Section almost brought a blush to his sallow cheek by calling him "Major" throughout this first address. One young lad who has only recently joined us went a little too far in the other direction and prefaced a question with "I say, Sarge!" The rest of us held our breath, but the lad's only rebuke was a silent and unwavering stare directed at him for the best part of a minute and having excellent effect.

The same telling technique was employed to put our own Mr. Corker in his place, not for any breach of etiquette, but because of his tendency to speak freely and exhaustively on any subject that happens to crop up. A burst of vigorous reminiscence about his own army days (when things were done quicker, better and more often) held up the Sergeant-major's discourse for some minutes; when the flow of words had at last died away under that shrivelling gaze, with the inevitable *coda* of ". . . I mean, if you see what I mean, I mean . . ." the Sergeant-major transferred his attention to the remainder of his audience and said, "I'll just repea' tha' bi' abou' the bayone'. . ." The treatment was so effective that there has been talk amongst our Section of trying it on Mr. Corker ourselves sometime, but it is doubtful whether anything will come of it. None of us has quite the right sort of eyes.

When the Sergeant-major talks to us there is a strange atmosphere of the schoolroom hovering over us all. Once more wondering Ignorance is dazzled by wonderful Knowledge; once more we feel a self-important glow when some special duty exalts us above the rest of the class (lending teacher our rifle, for instance, or hastening to pick up his fallen notebook); and although things have not quite reached the stage when we bring bunches of wild flowers and lay them adoringly before his army boots, there is a scuffle to hand him a cigarette when we are dismissed, and a rivalry for the distinction of driving him home, which must surely be a corresponding adult manifestation of the forgotten homage of youth.

He is a bloodthirsty little man, this khaki-clad schoolmaster, and the invective which he refrains from hurling at our heads is reserved for references to the enemy, singly or in the mass. The invader whose schemes it will be our joy to foil is always described by the Sergeant-major as "—— Jerry," and this without any word of apology or false diffidence. It is "—— Jerry" who is hiding behind the "bushy-topped trees" in the middle distance; "—— Jerry" who is watching for our slightest movement as we lie in the "tussocky grass" in the left foreground; "—— Jerry" who dives from the air on to our scanty cover beside the "rail-and-post fence," or has established a machine-gun nest in the "red-roofed building, right centre." The highly-coloured picture of the English countryside which the Sergeant-major has pinned up on the wall of our classroom is, in fact (and to use his own words), "stinking with —— Jerries." The two main things to remember, he tells us as his last word for the day, are that "—— Jerry" will shoot us if we don't shoot him, and that "—— Jerry" will run a mile at the sight of a bayonet—provided of course that we grimace fiercely enough and shout loudly enough as we run along behind it.

After the first shock to our illusions we found ourselves on the whole much impressed by our Sergeant-major. Some of us are even a little envious. Mr. Punnitt and Mr. Benn, for example, the glory still in their eyes as they watched our Section Leader drive him proudly away to his long-poured-out dinner, both declared that if they had been younger men they would have enlisted without hesitation, purely for the satisfaction of working up to be Sergeant-majors themselves. But little Mr. King, leaning on his bicycle and gazing after the receding car, shook his head doubtfully.

"Ah," said he, with the air of one who knows his limitations, even though others may not—"but 'tain't everyone as can do it. He's got the gift o' the gab, see—aye, and eddication, too!"

10

Our Patrols Were Active

It was a purely voluntary affair. Our Section Leader had made that clear from the beginning. If any of us preferred to waste a glorious moonlight night by the fireside, covering ourselves with tobacco-ash and yawning our heads off, then we were perfectly free to do so. If, on the other hand (and here our Section Leader had fixed us with a hypnotic eye), the Section turned out in full strength to give the exercise its support, then it would achieve three things: first, it would make its Leader a happy man; secondly, it would earn the undying respect of "A" Section, its collaborators for the occasion, and thirdly, it would benefit by an invigorating and educational experience, namely an hour's crawl on its bellies across the frozen moor . . .

The response was heartening, full marks for attendance only being snatched from us by the absence of Mr. Benn. Frankly, we were disappointed in Mr. Benn. There was some speculation whether his keenness had been losing its edge lately. Mr. Punnitt recalled significantly that after his last two hours' sentry-go Mr. Benn had confessed to having felt "not very comfortable out there"; true, there had been a raid on at the time and the sentry had been without cover or companionship, but the remark had not been well received, and was now feared to have been the first hint of a weakening morale.

It was the intervention of little Mr. King which put an end to these unfounded conjecturings. "You need to remember," he said, shaking his neat grey head reprovingly—"'e's not a young chap, Mr. Benn isn't; no, not for all 'im being so big-made!" And the gossips held their peace.

The exercise had been hatched up at a solemn Staff Talk between our Section Leader and Mr. Smirk, Leader of "A" Section. "A" Section was on duty that night and Mr. Smirk, thinking it high time that his men should have a taste of working in the dark (ever the privilege of the rank-and-file), had decided to take advantage of a full moon to let them down gently at their first attempt. However, the projected operations had grown to such magnitude during the preliminary planning that our own Section had finally been invited to take a hand. This would enable Mr. Smirk to leave an adequate force in the guard-room in case any less innocuous exercise should take shape in the neighbourhood, while still giving full scope to his military genius.

Our instructions were simple. It appeared (from information received) that a small number of the enemy was in possession of a certain mound, tumulus or strategic height some half-mile out across the moor. We were to approach this stronghold by stealth and bring about its downfall, taking prisoners, if possible. That was all.

We of "B" Section were a little hurt to learn that our function would be merely that of a decoy ("a bunch of ruddy red-herrings," as Mr. Corker had redundantly put it in the first sting of resentment), Mr. Smirk's plan having provided for the real glory to go to his own men. Our task was to approach the enemy unobtrusively until we were within earshot and then attract his attention by an orgy of twig-cracking, rifle-dropping and other intentional clumsiness so that "A" Section could sweep up from the rear, surprising and overpowering the foe with a minimum of bloodshed and delay.

After we had assimilated the details thoroughly,

politely congratulating Mr. Smirk on the adoption of tactics not scorned even by General Wavell, we buckled on our harness and synchronized our watches. (The strangers of "A" Section were entertained to see that little Mr. King's watch, substantially built and practically spherical, was produced from a worn cardboard-box and a quantity of soiled cotton-wool.) Then we adjusted our helmets to a rakish B.E.F. angle and passed out tensely into the silvery night.

On the edge of the moor our leaders said a last word to their men, wished each other good luck, and gravely shook hands. The battle was on. In sober confidence our Sections went their separate and premeditated ways.

For mere beginners at the game we didn't do too badly. Apart from the chattering of an imperfectly-fitting bayonet and an occasional crash as our Section Leader drew our attention to an ice-bound pool, the procession filed along inconspicuously enough. Our instructions to keep five yards between each man were at first respected to the inch, for although each of us felt confident of keeping his own bayonet out of mischief, there was a suspicion that the man behind might not be equally sure of himself. It was this uneasiness which presently played havoc with our formation, for little Mr. King, bringing up the rear, suddenly imagined that he was falling behind, and took a pace or two at the double; Mr. Tucker, hearing the quickening footfalls and fearing an impending flesh-wound, also broke into a precautionary lope, spreading the infection to Mr. Corker, who passed it on at a lurching trot to Mr. Curtis. Thus, after the first five minutes or so we proceeded behind our Leader in tightly-bunched formation. Fortunately he was too absorbed to be alive to his peril, and when he paused to give instructions he no doubt attributed our proximity to a burst of sprinting.

We approached our objective by an indirect route, chosen for the sake of the cover it afforded. Mr. Corker, on whom the ban of silence lay irksomely, soon began to announce that we were hopelessly lost. He had shot thousands of "rabbuts" on this very ground, he declared hoarsely, and was confident that every step was taking us farther from our goal. The commentary would have continued indefinitely but for a brisk trip across open country; this exhausted Mr. Corker's reserves of breath, and presently his misgivings were proved groundless, for two right-angle deflections from our line of progress had brought before our eyes the strategic height itself, softly silhouetted against the skyline. We subsided panting on the heather, gathering our strength for the final dash.

At this point Mr. Punnitt took the opportunity to untie a small parcel of provisions, and courteously invited the rest of us to join him in a snack. We were much impressed by his coolness. It was the sort of thing we had read about, we told ourselves, in agency messages about the Army of the Nile. Our Section Leader alone was grudging of admiration. Perhaps he feared that a concerted paroxysm of ungovernable indigestion might reveal our position; perhaps it was just that he could not reconcile the beauty of the night with the base materialism of a full-blooded beef sandwich. Whatever his reasons, he waved the offer aside and dispatched Mr. King and Mr. Tucker on reconnaissance with their first mouthfuls unmasticated.

They crept away obediently, and presently returned with the news that the mound was beyond doubt occupied.

"Beg to report," said Mr. Tucker formally, "at least two of the enemy in possession."

"Ah!" said our Section Leader, his suspicions confirmed.

"Talkin' fifteen to the dozen, they was!" said Mr. King, collapsing excitedly amongst us. "That's how we knew they was there, see? We could 'ear 'em but not see 'em! They was talkin' about rabbits——"

"Rabbuts?" said Mr. Corker, seizing the first opportunity to make himself useful—"why, that chumulus is alive with rabbuts; nothing *but* rabbuts on that chumulus. Well, I mean, take last Sunday, I mean, when we was out with guns, Jim Archer an' me; talk about rabbuts——"

Our Section Leader stirred sharply.

"Which way were they facing, Mr. Tucker?"

Mr. Tucker explained that as the enemy had not been visible it was difficult to say. From the sound of it they seemed to be facing away from us.

"Yes," said our Section Leader, taking in the situation—"follow me, men. If I lie down, do the same. Ready!"

He set out stealthily across the strip of exposed ground, and when his figure threatened to merge into the shadows, Mr. Corker led the rest of us in his wake. We had not covered more than fifty yards when Mr. Corker fell abruptly on his face. A second later we were all flattened in the heather, waiting for our Section Leader to rise again.

Several minutes passed; from the dimness ahead there came muffled cracklings, and the sound of some heavy object being laboriously moved; there were grunts and stifled exclamations. Then to Mr. Corker's horror and amazement, there ap-

". . . get me out of this blasted pit . . . !"

peared less than a yard from his face the sundered head of our Leader, hatless and wild-eyed, gleaming coldly in the moonlight. For the first time in his life Mr. Corker was at a loss for words; he could only return the Thing's hellish gaze. Then the tension was snapped suddenly.

"Don't lie there like a stuffed ape!" said the voice of our Section Leader. "*Get me out of this blasted pit!*"

The rest of us got him out. Mr. Corker was too shaken to take part. No further reference has been made to this incident—not, at any rate, in our Section Leader's hearing.

At the foot of the mound, in a tangle of brushwood and young fir-trees, we paused again. Above us, and facing in the direction from which "A" Section was scheduled to attack in exactly two minutes (by our synchronized watches), two standing figures were visible. A voice floated down to us clearly.

"But over yonder," it said—and an arm was raised to point—"beyond Gallows Top over towards Harry Cross's farm——"

"Noise!" commanded our Section Leader—"make a noise, for the lord's sake!" He began to thrash about him wildly with his rifle, and the rest of us threw ourselves into the game with zest. Bolts were rattled, young trees callously maimed, boots kicked frenziedly together; we cleared our throats raucously, made savage bayonet-lunges at the mound's defenceless sides, and set up a babel of primitive cries. Mr. Corker began a hysterical rendering of "I'm Dancing with Tears in My Eyes," but our Section Leader decided that we had now done what was necessary, and silenced us with a sharp word of command.

We looked upwards in the uncanny hush that followed. The two figures had not moved. The other voice was speaking.

"But suppose," it said, "you was to cut across Allen's forty-acre field——"

Our Section Leader all but wrung his hands. Thirty seconds from now Mr. Smirk would lead his men straight into the arms of the enemy. We stared at each other blankly. Then, just as the situation seemed lost, little Mr. King was brilliantly inspired to retrieve it. He had been eyeing the stronghold narrowly for some time, and suddenly he gave a start of recognition.

"Why!" he exclaimed delightedly—"if it isn't Mr. Benn, turned out after all!" He began to leap up the incline like a mountain goat. "Mr. Benn! *Mr. Benn!* It's me—it's Mr. King!"

The larger of the enemy turned and began to approach curiously. The other followed.

"Hallo, there, Mr. King!" boomed Mr. Benn's voice. "Blest if I hadn't forgotten all about you chaps, arguing with my friend Mr. Snape here.

Listen, now: if you wanted to get to Harry Cross's farm for a bit of rabbit-shooting——"

But Mr. King's work was done. Punctual to the second, "A" Section swarmed over the other side of the mound and crushed all resistance without a shot being fired.

II

Finding our Feet

At first we just called it "a route march," matter-of-factly and with varying pronunciations; we were airy about it to our wives, explaining that it was just one of those odd things soldiers had to do. That was before we marched it. While we were marching it we called it other things, and if anybody brings up the subject now it is referred to as "that Sunday morning," and we shift our boots about gently to see if our wounds are healed.

It was only six miles; three there and three back; this had better be confessed at once. Mr. Corker, who patrols that bit of road daily on an Automobile Association motor-cycle, had at first assessed the mileage at four and a quarter, but when he had paced it out he had to confess to a miscalculation on the part of his instruments. It was seven miles, he said, if it was an inch; and nobody contradicted him. If he had said seventy we should only have nodded and changed the subject.

There is a strip of nearby countryside which will in Certain Circumstances pass into our care, conjointly with a neighbouring platoon, and it was to study its military pros and cons that we were taken on this Sunday morning. We were a little late getting under way owing to some doubt amongst our officers whether a persistent dampness in the air could justly be regarded as rain. According to official arrangements, rain was to quash the outing; waterproof capes have not yet reached us in adequate numbers (we only have two), and our greatcoats, once wet, will steam merrily for days without getting appreciably drier.

It says much for the Platoon's keenness that not one of us made the weather an excuse for staying in bed, especially as it came out during the march that the temptation had crossed the minds of us all. It would have been so easy to say, when taxed with absenting ourselves from parade, "But it was raining!" As little Mr. King observed, delighted with his rights, "They couldn't have done nothing to you, neither!"

Actually, it was never properly decided whether we had paraded in drizzle or merely a drenching Scotch mist, but the major problem—whether we were to tramp the road or go back to our Sunday papers—was solved ingeniously by the Platoon Commander. After a quarter of an hour's conference with our Section Leaders, while the rest of us stood in the drizzle (or Scotch mist) explaining that we had scarcely tasted our breakfasts in our scamper to parade punctually, he gave judgment that as we were nearly wet through already we had better get on the move to stave off pneumonia. This sounded wiser at the time than it seemed when we thought it over afterwards, and we fell in smartly, grateful at being spared the vexation of doctor's bills.

"Platoon will advance in threes!" announced the Platoon Commander with flattering conviction—"Right . . . *tupp!*" We pivoted in our puddles. "Qui-i-i-ck . . . *mupp!*"

And off we *mupp-ed*.

This Platoon Commander was a visitor; his Platoon it is which will be collaborating with us in the prosecution of trespassers—for, alas! we cannot forgive them that trespass against us—and it seemed only fair that he should conduct the tour of our prospective battle-fields.

He had inspired confidence in us from the first; there was a certain dash about him, and his words of command had a whipcrack quality which startled us into unwonted unanimity. There was something rather special about his appearance too which we found mildly refreshing. Our own Platoon Commander is an older man, and a

"*. . . tends to smack a little of the sea . . .*"

nautical man; a lifetime spent at grips with the elements has bred in him an easy disregard for mere externals, and he has never taken quite kindly to khaki. His uniform, on those occasions when he can bring himself to wear it, tends to smack a little of the sea; sometimes his drab battle-dress is supplemented by a coarse navy-blue jacket such as old Peggotty used to wear (double-breasted, with six buttons a side and short narrow lapels); sometimes it is a sou'wester, or a dark cloth cap with ear-flaps buttoned on top, which singles him out from the landlubbers under his command.

But our leader to-day, marching a pace ahead of a galaxy of Section Leaders, who studied him no less closely than the rank and file that followed, seemed to us the very pattern of what a Platoon Commander should be.

His greatcoat was of a smoother, richer texture, its skirts falling elegantly from a skilfully-tailored waistline; the half-belt across the back lay flat and snug. After we had marched a quarter of a mile behind this coat we felt that our own, once our joy and pride, were gross, botched and unbecoming. His cap too had superior features; its lines were delicately graceful, and its badge and buttons were not garish with metal-polish but dark, dignified and in the best possible taste. When he ran back to see how many of us were still in step we saw that his coat's widespread lapels were rolled softly back to reveal nothing more or less than a collar and tie—sartorial accessories that our own Platoon Commander is rumoured to scorn sometimes even in civil life. And beneath his razor-edged trousers there marched before us not the clumsy leathern hooves that stumped all about us, but a pair of gleaming nut-brown shoes whose glory even the gathering drops of water could not dim.

"Gets 'isself up a treat, don't he?" said our little Mr. King. A plain man, Mr. King may have intended the remark disapprovingly; but its inflexion was one of envy.

We were all of us envious before very long. It came to us gradually. The greatcoat we admired, but did not covet; the streamlined cap we admired too, but reflected that our heads were probably kept just as warm by our own; it was not even the crease in the trousers, nor yet the collar and tie which slowly aroused in us a lust for possession; it was that pair of gleaming nut-brown shoes, rising and falling so lightly, so quietly.

They looked such comfortable shoes, such supple, flexible, tractable, well-trained, good-natured shoes. They reminded us of shoes we possessed ourselves—shoes we had had to leave at home just because we were not Platoon Commanders.

Curiously enough our early conversation had

become almost exclusively devoted to footwear shortly after the order to march at ease had loosened our tongues. We had commented to each other (during the first five hundred yards) on the surprising easiness of our feet. . . . We had heard such dreadful tales about army boots, we said to each other laughingly (during the first five hundred yards), that we had really been a little nervous about taking ours out on the road for the first time. We agreed with each other that they really were wonderfully comfortable boots, so strong, so hard-wearing, so firm about the ankle. We exchanged useful hints about wearing two pairs of socks, or soaking the uppers in paraffin, and explained at length our own particular systems of doing up the laces. We became really friendly with men in other Sections whom we had scarcely spoken to before—all because we were so delighted with our boots. But after a time the topic seemed to become tame; after the first mile it became painful; we turned to other matters, but the conversation was forced, and presently long silences fell upon us, while we tried to tread gently, gazing with increasing fixedness at those pliable, beautiful nut-brown shoes.

The first hint that all was not well with the

Platoon's feet came from Mr. Benn. His voice boomed over our heads from the rear rank.

"Do you know,'' said Mr. Benn, "I reckon I'm starting a —— blister!"

Mr. Punnitt, at his side, laughed bitterly.

"Only one?" he said.

After this the conversation revived again. Our first consideration was to retract as vehemently as possible everything we had been saying about our boots. Next we turned our attention to the Ministry of Supply, and were unnecessarily and unjustly outspoken on the subject of Government contractors in such notorious districts as Leicester and Northampton. Finally the several streams of our grievances merged into a fast-flowing recital of individual blisters and (to quote Mr. Punnitt) "blebs."

Mr. Benn and Mr. Punnitt, having been the first to be honest about their feet, went on to prove themselves by their behaviour to be the hardest hit. During the hundred yards before we halted at our destination Mr. Punnitt hopped on alternate feet, causing the Platoon Commander (in his comfortable shoes) to call out "Left, right! Left, right!" though without turning round to witness Mr. Punnitt's anguish. Mr. Benn, dimly remembering perhaps the popular paintings by Lady Butler depicting the common soldier enduring hardship, tried to convert his rifle into a crutch. The experiment was rendered null and void on account of his great height, and he only succeeded in packing his rifle-muzzle with mud.

The rest of us were suffering also, but not having the luck to be in the rear rank we were subject to the surveillance of several young children who had chosen some time before to march gravely beside the leading ranks, pushing wooden boxes on wheels and expressing frank views on our general deportment. This unofficial contingent did useful work in warning us when we were in danger of being run down by overtaking traffic, but could otherwise have been dispensed with cheerfully.

When we had ultimately limped our way to a grassy eminence, from which the Platoon Commander was to indicate to us noteworthy features of the rain-dimmed plain below, it was not surprising that we were in no state to comprehend the full gist of his observations. We recognized that the matter should have had our unstinted attention, and yet somehow our hearts were not in it. They were, if the truth be told, in our stout, stiff, spiteful and malicious army boots, doing their best to burst open the laces. And in the minds of us all was the frightful thought that when our instruction was over the homeward road still lay before us.

The instruction was over in next to no time. The rain was thickening over the plain, and the course of the river which was to form our line of defence was so disguised by the February floods that even our instructor himself found his key landmarks obscured. This deliverance from prolonged tuition would have delighted us at any other time—when our feet had not cried aloud for rest; as it was, the Platoon Commander's decision to make for home almost without delay evoked stifled groans from most of us and frank dismay from Messrs. Benn and Punnitt. Misconstruing these expressions of disappointment, the Platoon Commander hastened to assure us that we should be allowed to march out again on the first fine Sunday morning. He failed to detect the bitterness in our chorus of thanks as we straggled painfully back to the main road.

The children who had accompanied us on the outward journey again fell in enthusiastically beside us. No doubt they were wearing their own boots. It was due entirely to their vigilance that we avoided being mown down by a country bus which presently overtook and passed us, splashing us to the waist; to their vigilance also was due the detection of Mr. Benn's fearful symmetry in one of the bus's back seats. Crouching in his shadow were the figures of Mr. Punnitt and an unknown sufferer of "D" Section who had joined them in desertion.

12

Men of Steel

For some time now our equipment has included a long blue-bladed piece of cutlery. Its cutting-edge, as Mr. Benn the butcher was quick to discern, is nothing to write home about; but that, so to speak, is not the point.

Official communications for some reason call this weapon a "side-arm," but to many of us it appears indistinguishable from a bayonet. It was indeed referred to us as such by our visiting Sergeant-major in his very last talk to us, when we were schooled in "whipping 'em out and whopping 'em on," but owing to an unfortunate contretemps were taken no farther along the road to gory glory.

Sadly, it must be recorded that our bayonets were instrumental in losing our Sergeant-major for us. His demonstration took place in the school yard, and there was present no less a personage than the Company Commander himself. Now, Company Commanders are busy men, especially on

Sunday mornings, and this no doubt explains why ours was trying to kill two birds with one stone by studying not only the lecturer, but the lecturees; not having brought a notebook with him it was understandable then, that when some point about our behaviour or appearance seemed to him not all it might be he should decide to take it up with the Sergeant-major there and then. He had perhaps had scant experience of Sergeant-majors; or possibly our lecturer had had scant experience of Company Commanders; at any rate, when he (our Company Commander) had interrupted the Sergeant-major in his discourse (*a*) to point out that one of us had his haversack over the wrong shoulder, (*b*) to inquire whether our badges were fastened on with stitches or safety-pins, and (*c*) to suggest that the yellow gloves affected by a member of "D" Section might offer a tempting target on a moonlight night, the Sergeant-major was seen to be struggling with a powerful emotion; this got the upper hand when his attention was finally drawn, in a gentle but resounding voice, to two unfastened buttons on his own tunic; he dropped the bayonet in a puddle, trod on it heavily, and dismissed the parade. Then he saluted a point three inches above our

Company Commander's head and marched smartly away, never to return.

A week or two later, when our Company Commander also had severed his connection with us, as Company Commanders will, we tried to lure our instructor back again. We sent a deputation, but he only looked bayonets at it and shook his head. It was plain that the association of ideas would have been unendurable.

So we began to cast about in our minds for a means of furthering our education. To stick a bayonet in the end of a rifle is one thing: to stick it in something else is another. At last our spies came to us with news of a certain Sergeant stationed with a lonely searchlight unit: it appeared that he would welcome a little entertainment in the long dark evenings, so we rode out to see him the following week, round about alert-time, our side-arms by our sides.

We found him awaiting us in a bleak and under-furnished hut—and not alone. Another Sergeant was with him. The pair of them laid end to end would only have made about one and a half standard-size Sergeants, for one was so tall that Mr. Benn was practically dwarfed, while the other had to direct his head upwards at an angle of forty-five degrees to return the "Good evening" of little Mr. King. It may have been this unusually pleasing state of affairs that led Mr. King to strike up a friendship with the small Sergeant; or it may have been that at the cost of a cigarette and a kind word he hoped to ingratiate himself, and thus ensure that his shortcomings with the bayonet would be overlooked. If this was the case, he soon found himself to be barking up the wrong tree, for his gnome-like friend was only present in the capacity of stooge, Aunt Sally, or impersonator-of-the-enemy: his gigantic colleague was, we learned, the man to watch and listen to.

Our instructor, though considerably above his pupils' average height, was considerably below their average age. Sensible of this, and being pleasantly free from airs of any kind, he began by saying diffidently that he expected many of us knew more about the bayonet than he did. A reminiscent "Ah-h-h!" from Volunteer Walker, "C" Section's gnarled veteran, was the only comment on this, and happily the rest of us were spared the temptation of acting a lie; for after this diffident overture the Sergeant twitched Mr. Curtis's rifle from his hand as if it had been a fountain-pen and launched into his subject-matter without further delay.

Unarmed and lounging, this giant in khaki had seized our attention from the start. Now he riveted it. The bayonet from the nearest scabbard on his left was flashed out and flicked on to the end of Mr. Curtis's rifle in an instant. A second later he had issued and executed the "On guard" command and was standing before and above us, as reassuring and unshakeable as the Statue of Liberty. Half a second after that he was lounging again. "That," he explained, "is the 'On guard' position." We nodded, and tried to see ourselves doing it. One or two of us caught the eye of Volunteer Walker. He nodded also, with an appreciative light in his eye.

The address then proceeded. Both the text and the illustrations were whirled at us throughout with such rapidity that while our minds bounded clumsily onwards in an attempt to absorb the last remark but three, our eyes were watching for the moment when, it seemed, the man must twiddle the rifle round on his finger by the trigger-guard, like the check-shirted characters in Western pictures. Certainly the thing seemed no bigger than a six-shooter in his tremendous hands, and when it whipped through the air with a whirring noise we began to think of some way to slip on our steel helmets unostentatiously, against the time when it should fly from his grasp and bowl us over like ninepins.

He had a great theatrical sense, this Sergeant. He was not so much an Ainley, a Tearle, a Hardwicke, as a Ruth Draper. Such was his skill at portraying British cold steel in action that before ten minutes had passed we saw the wooden floor of our lecture-hall strewn with gasping and perforated members of the opposition, disarmed, dismayed and—other "dis's." In the conjuring up of this encouraging vision the subsidiary role played by the small Sergeant should receive notice. The cue for his entrance was a muttered aside—"Okay, Joe," and upon this he came and stood a yard from the leading man's bayonet.

We then witnessed a thrilling performance. Assuming a mien of alarming ferocity the tall Sergeant leapt forward with a "long point," followed with a "short point," leapt onwards with a "jab," a "butt-stroke," a "slash" and another butt-stroke. At some point of the advance he also stamped on his adversary's face, but this, we gathered, didn't really count. When it was over, at any rate, he only claimed six certainly destroyed, though we felt that there would have been others unlikely to return to their base. It was the small Sergeant, of course, who was taking all this punishment. His task was to represent half a dozen ill-starred opponents advancing in single file, and it will be appreciated that the feat called for great delicacy of footwork, not only to step sharply to one side to avoid losing his ears, nose or scalp, but also to step backwards ready to impersonate the next victim. Throughout, he was utterly impassive and spoke no word. Even during his sixth characterization, when, knowing the scene to be at an end, he lay on the floor placidly as the blade whizzed into the boards beside his left cheek, he made no comment, not even suggesting that his vanquisher ought to take on somebody his own size. Some of us were, at this time, toying with the idea of trying to borrow him for a little practice on our own account when we were sufficiently far advanced.

"Okay, Joe," said the aggressor, wiping first his brow and then his bayonet (probably in the order laid down in Regulations), and the enemy rose and retired dispassionately to his corner.

Inviting us to agree with him that bayonet-fighting was the simplest thing in the world, our instructor now suggested that we should prove this by trying it for ourselves. We braced ourselves and avoided each other's eye; one or two of the more eager ones made as if to fix bayonets, but he held up an enjoining hand. "I wouldn't," he said—"just use your imagination." And the rest of us sighed in concerted relief; we were lined up on either side of the hut, and even with nothing more penetrating than a blunt muzzle waiting to fly at us we felt the situation uncomfortable enough.

"On—*guard!*"

We slapped our left feet forward, hurled up our rifles, most of us managing to catch them in the other hand. (An exception was little Mr. King. He hit on the ingenious idea of dropping his rifle and taking so long to recover it that the battle had ceased to surge about him by the time he was ready to take part in it.) We stood for a moment trembling slightly—no doubt from excitement—and then, at the word of command, the building shuddered from the shock of our advancing feet and the air was filled with flailing rifles and leaping men. We had got as far as the first butt-stroke before we realized that something was happening that had not figured in the syllabus—something that froze us in our tracks, butts poised to dispose of our fourth victim, but unable to deal the blow.

Above the din there had risen a hideous cry.

It might have been the squealing of phantom swine, fearing for their phantom necks; the death-gurgle of a whole family of hyenas; the demoniac shriek of an earth-bound spirit, or the caterwauling of a giant cat yielding up its ninth life to the devil. Any of these things, and many more unthinkable things, it could have been. Actually it was nothing more than the war-cry of Volunteer Walker. Bounding across the floor to the accompaniment of this piece of self-encouragement and mortally wounding a board in the opposite wall by driving his rifle through a knot-hole, this seasoned campaigner now fell silent and became suddenly conscious of the white faces and bulging eyes surrounding him. He appeared to be embarrassed, and fell to scratching a speck of rust from his trigger-guard with a horny finger-nail.

The tall Sergeant took out a handkerchief and wiped the back of his neck before breaking the silence.

"Yes," he said. His voice was not wholly under control. "Perhaps I should have mentioned about setting up a bit of a shout during the Charge; but it seems you'll be able to get some tuition on that nearer home. What about a pint, Joe?"

"I'll say," said Joe, and the pair of them made a painstakingly unhurried exit, noting Volunteer Walker's position and passing by on the other side.

13

Garden Party

To spend a sunny morning stretched at full length on a damp lawn may not at first glance seem a notable contribution towards the national effort. Yet our Squad was not being unpatriotic when it so occupied itself last Sunday, even though not one of its members so much as turned a spadeful of earth during the whole of its stay. In point of fact more spadefuls of earth than necessary had already been turned by our agents, the regulars, in anticipation of our visit.

Two large oblong holes the regulars had dug for us, so deep that Mr. Benn could have stood in one and only been visible from the chest upwards, while little Mr. King, standing in the other, would have been concealed from his steel helmet downwards. As it happened, neither of these Volunteers stood in the holes at all; eighteen inches of cocoa-coloured water had stolen a march on them, so they lay on the grass with the rest of us, training their rifles vigilantly on the main road where the villagers plodded unsuspectingly to church.

The garden was our responsibility, though not our property; we had had it commandeered for us in that authoritative way which so endears the Army to its prospective protégés. The owners, from the damp little house on our right, peered at us nervously through their yellowish lace curtains, sometimes from the downstairs windows, sometimes from up above. We felt that they referred to us amongst themselves as "the military" and vaguely held us to blame for the disappearance of other sunny Sundays when plump tourists in glittering cars used to waddle up to the door, attracted by the board outside which said bluntly "TEA'S."

It was not a beautiful garden, and yet for our purpose it had several not unlovely features. It afforded cover from view, and will afford even more if the invasion waits until the hedges are thick with leaf. It will afford cover from fire too when the water has been drained away from our nice deep holes. From our garden we have an arc of fire (how one slips into using these technicalities!) covering the entrance to or exit from The Bridge—it depends on which way the battle decides to surge. The Bridge is our Platoon's very own charge, and when we learned this a short time ago we felt dimly that we were being done out of our fun, for we all knew that the only thing to be done to bridges is to blow them up. Too, too simple. And although we did look forward to an interesting lottery to decide who should light the fuse and be the last to run, we felt too that better use might have been made of our skill in the more subtle forms of warfare.

Probably in deference to our views, which must somehow have reached the ear of the authorities, it was later decided that the bridge should not be blown up after all; and it is an odd commentary on the way the soldier's mind works that this decision provoked spirited inquiries: Why not? There was a hint of jealousy in it perhaps; Ketterbourne and Little Snelling and Maidsworth each had a nice bridge to blow up—why shouldn't we?

"I've no doubt," said little Mr. King with unwonted malice, "that there's somebody 'as *shares* in it."

"Shares?" said Mr. Corker.

"Money," said Mr. King, wagging his head darkly—"you know how it is with wars!"

Mr. Corker was out of his depth for once, and hastened to take the stage by reciting a generation-old grievance against a regimental paymaster, proving at some length that the National Debt included fifteen pounds of his, Mr. Corker's, back pay.

The explanation of our suddenly ceasing to be dynamiters was never given us. The authorities are like that.

However, from our hiding-place we cover the end of the bridge—the very spot where enemy tanks will be persuaded by ingenious means to disembark their crews, all curiosity. That spot, as Mr. Corker said with satisfaction, will be the last thing the enemy gets really curious about.

Bridges, to serve any useful purpose, need water to flow under them. Ours is no exception. Water not only flowed under it on this particular Sunday morning, but round and about it, and in some places all but over it. This was the same water which lapped gently at two sides of our garden; which had poured sluggishly into our nice deep holes, and which now, as we lay there waiting, oozed up through the grass to make dark patches on our knees and elbows and to take the shine off our buttons. And here it might be explained just what it was that we were waiting for, lying on the lawn, soaking up the floods into our greatcoats.

We were waiting, as we have so often waited, for a High Officer. Not only our Squad, our Platoon, our Company, our Battalion, but every Volunteer in the county was waiting—for this same High Officer. He was giving up his morning to motoring about the countryside, seeing if he could see us: it was up to us to see that he could not.

As he had only three hours allotted to him to satisfy himself that every Home Guard in the county was invisible at his Action Station, we felt fairly safe in assuming that he would ride past our muzzles at some speed; but in spite of this we took no risks, and if any of us happened to be on our feet when a conveyance of any kind rounded the approach to the bridge, we fell suddenly and squelchingly to the ground. It is rumoured that a High Officer on inspection is apt to resort to any kind of low trick, and even the spectacle of a dead horse being transported to its lonely funeral (waving a nonchalant hind leg in farewell to a harsh world) filled us with mistrust. Might this not be an ingenious deceit? What had happened at Troy? But little Mr. King recognized the mourner-driver as a business acquaintance and addressed him with a cheerful "Now then, Josh! Meat ration goin' up next week?" We breathed again. It was not only suspense which had made us hold our breath.

All morning we waited there, not knowing whether the moment of our testing had gone or was yet to come. All morning we lay there in our garden, or bobbed cautiously up and down. The waters lapped dismally about us, and the yellowish lace curtains on our right flank twitched nervously. It was important that these twitchings should not distract our attention from still another window on the opposite side of the road, where Platoon Headquarters was established in a derelict cottage. There, in an upper room, was installed our Platoon Commander with, no doubt, his maps, codes, Platoon rations and other military secrets, and from that upper room we knew that there might be displayed, some time during the morning, a red flag (kindly lent by the Automobile Association through the good offices of Mr. Corker). The red flag would mean GAS, and when it came into view we were to take "appropriate action" (beloved phrase).

A downstairs room of the cottage constituted

our Field Hospital, and even as we lay watching we knew that a camp-bed was in that room, twirling about idly in six inches of water until such a time as the weight of a casualty should bring it to anchor. Mr. Tucker, who had looked through the window, had told us this, adding that any patient tended in our Field Hospital would stand an excellent chance of being buried at sea.

It was little Mr. King who first saw the red flag. The rest of us had been improving the shining hour by hurling large stones into the water, feeling that experience gained at hand-grenade practice might excuse a few not very ostentatious splashes. Little Mr. King, who had been discouraged by failing to clear the lawn with his first grenade, had rotated on his stomach so as to face Headquarters. Suddenly he sprang to his feet with a startling cry of "I see red!" and when our first rush of concern had evaporated we followed his gaze. There was certainly a smudge of red on the window-sill, but it was a half-hearted sort of signal and there was some doubt whether it could be a signal at all; possibly the flag had merely been laid down on the sill by somebody as tired of waiting as we were.

It was decided that Mr. Benn, whose long legs would carry him over the road in next to no time, should be sent to ask respectfully whether we were undergoing a gas-attack or not. We watched him vanish round the back of the cottage, and waited anxiously. To our astonishment he did not return, and when ten minutes had passed it was thought

"... *failing to clear the lawn with his first grenade* ..."

that Mr. Corker should be sent to investigate. It occurred to us that Headquarters might have been surprised and overthrown from the rear. Those things did happen. It was five minutes later that we began to be genuinely alarmed, for Mr. Corker did not come back either. The cottage across the road began to seem as sinister as the silent fort in *Beau Geste*.

Presently little Mr. King, with a light in his eyes that might have meant anything from heroism to despair, rose to his feet, took up his equipment and followed in the wake of his lost comrades. In admiration and bewilderment we watched him go. Vainly we waited for his return.

After another ten minutes of almost unbearable tension Mr. Punnitt got up and slung his rifle over his shoulder. He said he didn't know whether the rest of us were aware of it, but the path leading to the rear of Headquarters also led, if pursued far enough, to the rear of a humble inn called (with an apt flavour) "The Dashing White Sergeant"; so that if—*if*, said Mr. Punnitt, the morning's exercise should by any chance have been brought to a close and some little hitch in communications should have prevented our party's being notified, then it was possible, just possible, that Volunteers Benn, Corker and King might have stumbled (quite by accident) upon it.

Perhaps the starter's pistol for an Olympic Games sprint has occasionally sent men off the mark faster than Mr. Punnitt's words sent the remnant of our Squad across that road, but it is doubtful. In the crowded bar of "The Dashing White Sergeant" we found not only our comrades, very much alive, but the entire Platoon. Our Platoon Commander, in return for information as to where he was likely to have mislaid his red flag, told us that the High Officer had inspected our territory two hours before; he also apologized handsomely that his Cease Fire orders should have failed to reach us.

However, our chagrin was in part alleviated when we learnt that the High Officer had been so impressed with our feats of concealment that he had strongly suspected us of not having turned out at all. And this, one or two of us alleged, would have made the exercise just as much of a success.

"Although," Mr. Punnitt said afterwards— "it was a very good glass of beer at the 'Sergeant.' I used to drop in there of an evening before I—er— when I was—er—well, in my young days, shall we say?"

And he patted his armlet affectionately.

OVERLEAF

particulars of publications
of similar interest
issued by

GEORGE ALLEN & UNWIN LTD
LONDON: 40 MUSEUM STREET, W.C.1
CAPE TOWN: 73 ST. GEORGE'S STREET
TORONTO: 91 WELLINGTON STREET WEST
BOMBAY: 15 GRAHAM ROAD, BALLARD ESTATE
WELLINGTON, N.Z.: 8 KINGS CRESCENT, LOWER HUTT
SYDNEY, N.S.W.: AUSTRALIA HOUSE, WYNYARD SQUARE

Bomb Doors Open: and other Radio War Dramas

by Cecil McGivern

La. Cr. 8vo. *Illustrated* *7s. 6d.*

Here are the radio feature programmes of a very successful series printed exactly as they were first typed for the producer, actors, effects men and engineers, whose job was to put them into the microphones which led to loudspeakers all over the world. The reader is thus able to read the stories of "ordinary people doing extraordinary jobs" and to see at the same time the "build-up" that gives reality to these feature programmes. The very style of these scripts—quiet and restrained, no purple passages—reveal the character and work of those who are doing great things in a matter-of-fact, almost casual, fashion. The contents are: (1) Bombers Over Berlin, (2) Fighter Pilot, (3) East Coast Convoy, (4) Bomb Doors Open, (5) Women Hitting Back, (6) Battle of Britain.

Lights of Freedom

Edited by Allan Michie and Walter Graebner

Demy 8vo. *Fully Illustrated* *10s. 6d.*

Here is another volume of personal stories of the war. The same qualities that made *Their Finest Hour* so popular are present in this volume, and in some ways it is even more dramatic than the first book. Walter Graebner contributes a brilliant account of the scene at a night fighter station when London had a particularly heavy raid last May, when our fighter planes and A.A. batteries disposed of thirty-three enemy planes. Sixteen magnificent photographs illustrate the section describing the great part being played by women. One story describes how a Coventry surgeon and his staff worked magnificently through one of the worst raids on the city. Throughout the book we get vivid glimpses of those who, working and enduring with quiet simple courage, are carrying the Lights of Freedom and living through Their Finest Hour.

A.R.P. and All That

AND OTHER WAR-TIME STORIES

An Anthology selected by C. Kent Wright. *Foreword by* Admiral Sir E. R. G. R. Evans. *Illustrated by* Eve Sheldon-Williams.

Cr. 8vo. *Second Impression* *2s. 6d.*

"At the end of a long, long day wrestling with shelter problems your book came in, and it made me laugh. Considering the frame of mind I was in, I can't think of higher praise."—ELLEN WILKINSON

10